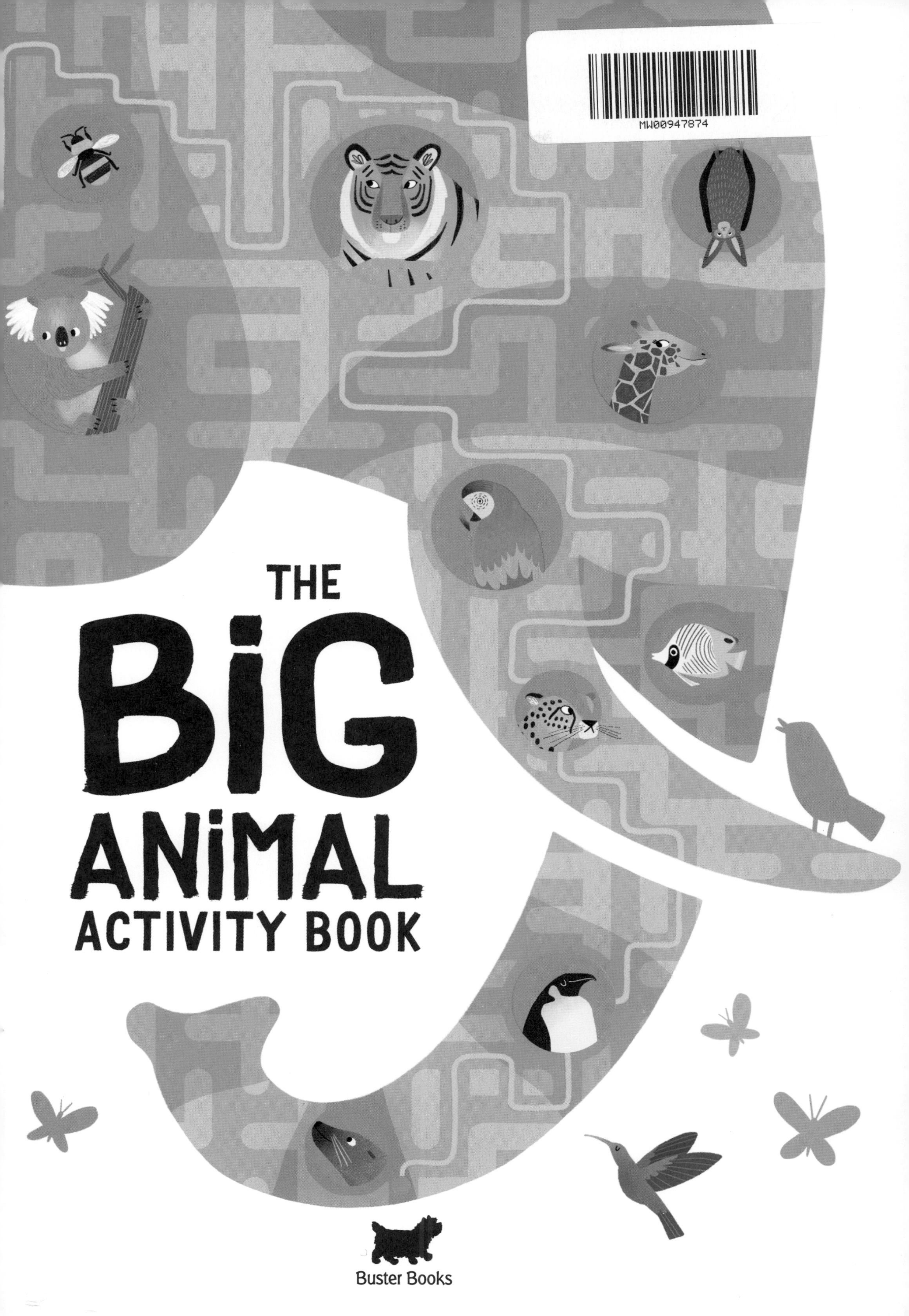
THE
BiG
ANiMAL
ACTIVITY BOOK
Buster Books

ILLUSTRATED BY JEAN CLAUDE

WRITTEN & EDITED BY FRANCES EVANS
DESIGNED BY ZOE BRADLEY
COVER DESIGNED BY JOHN BIGWOOD

First published in Great Britain in 2020 by Buster Books, an imprint of
Michael O'Mara Books Limited, 9 Lion Yard, Tremadoc Road, London SW4 7NQ

 www.mombooks.com/buster  Buster Books  @BusterBooks

ISBN: 978-1-78055-631-4

3 5 7 9 10 8 6 4 2

This book was printed in June 2020 by Leo Paper Products Ltd,
Heshan Astros Printing Limited, Xuantan Temple Industrial Zone,
Gulao Town, Heshan City, Guangdong Province, China.

PAW-SOME PUZZLES

Have you ever wondered why bats hang upside down, which bird builds the biggest nest or how long an anteater's tongue is? Well, you're about to find out.

The puzzles in this book will introduce you to some amazing animals from all around the world – from creatures you might spot in your garden to critically endangered species that exist only in a few protected places. By completing each challenge, you can learn about the lives of the incredible animals we share our planet with. Guide a herd of zebras through a migration maze, match up pairs of dancing cranes, search for rare creatures in Borneo's rainforest and much more!

Along the way, you can discover hundreds of fascinating facts about the animal kingdom, such as why okapis have smelly feet, how chimps use tools to get food and why satin bowerbirds love the colour blue.

When you've finished, you can check your answers to all the puzzles at the back of the book on pages 118–128.

Now, grab a pencil and get ready for loads of furry and feathered puzzle fun.

MACAW SEQUENCES

Which bird would come next in each of the following sequences?

Macaws are large, colourful parrots that live in Central and South America. There are thought to be around 17 different species – from the hyacinth macaw, the largest parrot in the world, to the Spix's macaw, the rarest bird in the world.

Macaws live in family groups of around 10–30 birds. They normally pair up for life. Partners will share food and groom one another to strengthen their bond.

TAMARIN TEASER

Can you spot ten differences between these pictures of golden lion tamarins?

Golden lion tamarins are a rare species of monkey found in the rainforests along Brazil's Atlantic coast.

Families of tamarins live together in the treetops. Males help the females to raise their young.

JAVAN RHINO JIGSAW

Which of the tiles below is not from this picture of a Javan rhino and its calf?

These rhinos live in tropical rainforests on the island of Java in Indonesia. They have a single, small horn and thick, grey skin that looks like armour.

A.

D.

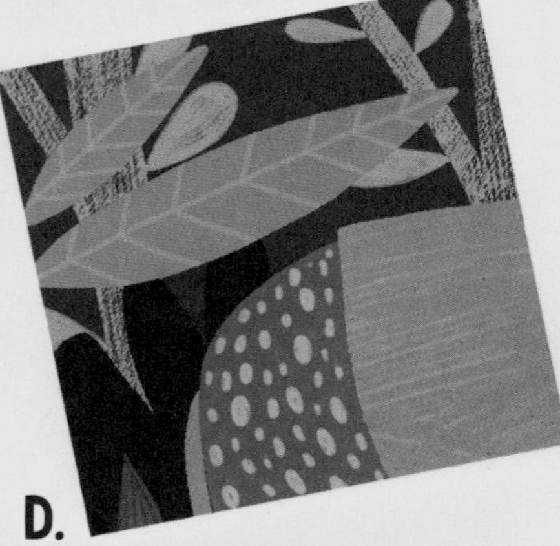

B.

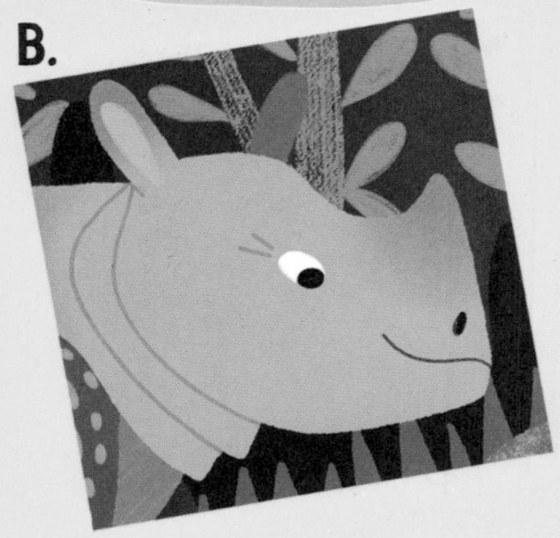

C.

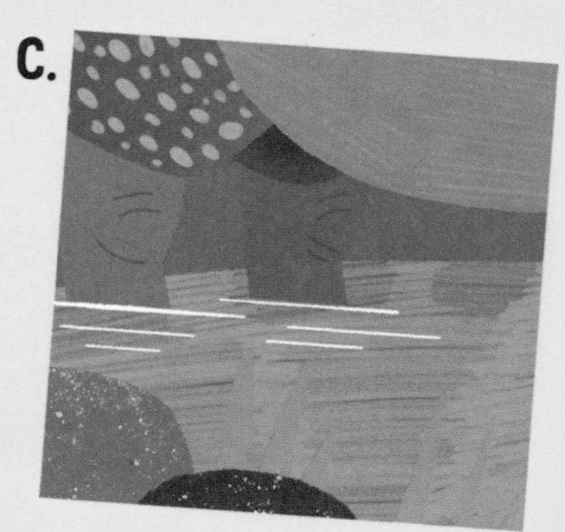

Only 58–68 Javan rhinos are thought to be alive today, making them one of the most endangered animals in the world.

SUMATRAN TIGER SUMS

These tigers live in remote forests on the Indonesian island of Sumatra. Solve the calculation chains below to discover some key stats about them. Start with the number on the left and perform each sum in turn to get the final result.

140 ÷ 2 - 60 x 2 =
the age these tigers can reach in the wild.

100 ÷ 2 - 20 ÷ 10 =
the average number of cubs a female will give birth to. Cubs remain with their mother for about two years, and then leave to find a territory of their own.

10 x 20 + 80 ÷ 2 =
the approximate weight of an adult male in kilograms. Sumatran tigers are the smallest subspecies of tiger in the world.

5 + 16 x 10 + 190 =
the number of Sumatran tigers thought to be left in the wild. Their population has more than halved since the 1970s.

TANGLED TWIGS
Untangle the twigs to work out what each chimpanzee is having for breakfast.
Chimpanzees sometimes use sticks and twigs to help them get food that's hard to reach, such as ants, termites and honey. They're thought to learn these skills from their parents when they're young.
A.
B.
C.
HONEY
TERMITES
ANTS
Different families of chimps use tools in different ways. While some use twigs to 'fish' for insects, others use stones to crack open nuts.

A FLOCK OF FLAMINGOS

How many lesser flamingos can you count on this lake?

Lesser flamingos are the smallest species of flamingo. They are mainly found in East Africa. Around 500,000 pairs are thought to live and breed on Lake Natron in Tanzania – this is the largest group of birds in the world!

By living in large groups, flamingos can protect themselves from predators. The birds will move together as a group if they feel threatened.

ODD BAT OUT
Can you find the one bat that looks different to the rest?
A place where bats rest is called a 'roost'. Bats normally roost in large groups, clinging to the ceiling of a cave or building using their back legs.
Unlike birds, bats cannot lift off from the ground when they take flight. Hanging upside down allows them to let go and 'fall' into flight.

NUTS ABOUT NUTS

These three red squirrels are collecting food in preparation for winter. One squirrel has stored its acorns in the tree, another has hidden them under the bush and another has buried them under the boulder. Their stores are three different sizes. Can you use the following clues to work out where each squirrel has stored its food and how big each squirrel's store is?

1. Squirrel B has a larger store than Squirrel A.
2. Squirrel A has not stored its acorns in the tree.
3. The store buried under the boulder is the smallest.
4. Squirrel A's store is not the smallest.

Red squirrels do not hibernate, so they need to collect a large store of food in the autumn to keep them going during the winter months, when food is harder to find.

A.

B.

C.

Red squirrels do not bury their food at random. They choose particular places, which they remember and return to.

WHERE'S THE WALLABY?

Can you spot the little grey wallaby in this troop of red kangaroos?

Kangaroos and wallabies are both 'marsupials' – meaning mothers carry their babies in pouches on their stomachs.

At 1.5–2 m tall, the red kangaroo is the world's largest marsupial. Wallabies are smaller – they vary from 30 cm to 1 m in height.

BAFFLED BIRDS

These busy satin bowerbirds can't remember whose bower is whose. The object in each bird's beak is identical to an item on one of the bowers. Study the pictures closely to match each bird with the correct bower.

Satin bowerbirds are found throughout eastern Australia. To attract females, male bowerbirds build a beautiful construction out of sticks, known as a bower.

Male satin bowerbirds decorate their bowers with colourful objects. These can range from feathers, shells and flowers to bottle tops, pegs and straws. It's thought the birds favour blue objects because they match the colour of their feathers.

SALMON MAZE

Help the salmon travel upstream to the lake to lay their eggs. Avoid the grizzly bears and any other obstacles as you go.

Salmon live in both salt water and fresh water. They are born in rivers and swim out to the sea as adults. When it's time for them to lay their own eggs (or 'spawn') they travel back to the river in which they were born.

The fish encounter many obstacles on their journey home. They have to swim against the current, through rapids, jump up waterfalls and avoid predators such as grizzly bears.
FINISH
The arrival of the salmon is important for the grizzly bears. The bears need to eat a huge amount of food in order to survive their hibernation during the winter months. Feeding on protein-rich salmon helps them to gain weight before they begin their long sleep.

ODD PENGUIN OUT

Can you spot the little Adélie penguin among this colony of Emperor penguins? It looks very different to its giant cousins.

There are 18 recognized species of penguin, but the Emperor and Adélie are the only ones that live in Antarctica all year round. Emperor penguins are the largest species of penguin – an adult Emperor penguin can be almost as tall as a six-year-old child – and Adélie penguins are the smallest.

Adélie penguins might be little but they're tough. They will attack potential predators, such as seals, if they feel threatened. They've even been known to slap human researchers with their flippers!

Temperatures in Antarctica can be as low as -60°C. To keep warm, Emperor penguins huddle together in large groups. The birds have thick layers of feathers and fat to help conserve heat. Their flippers and beaks are also proportionally smaller than those of other penguins, which stops them from losing too much heat.

SLOTH SILHOUETTE

Which of these silhouettes matches this sloth exactly?

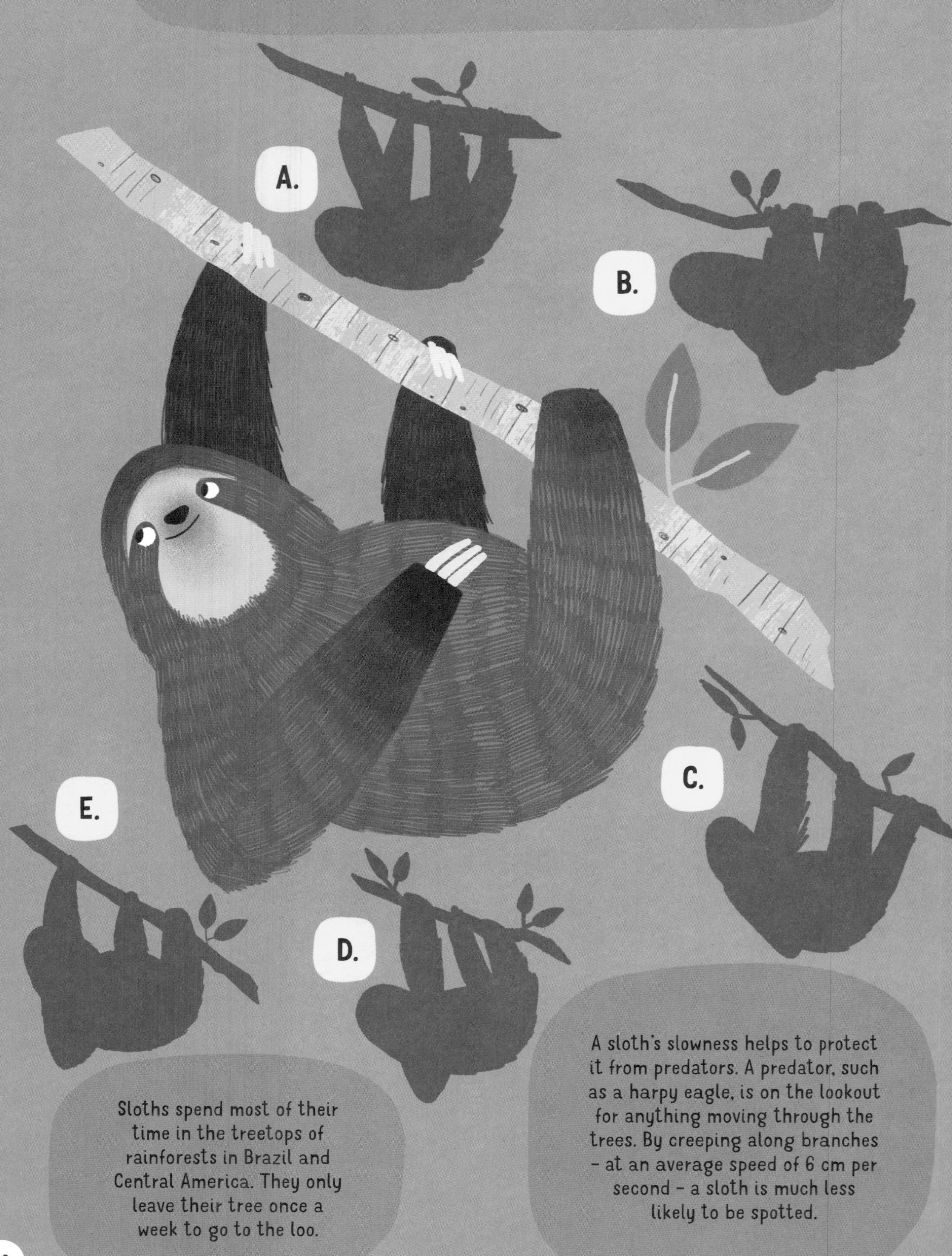

Sloths spend most of their time in the treetops of rainforests in Brazil and Central America. They only leave their tree once a week to go to the loo.

A sloth's slowness helps to protect it from predators. A predator, such as a harpy eagle, is on the lookout for anything moving through the trees. By creeping along branches – at an average speed of 6 cm per second – a sloth is much less likely to be spotted.

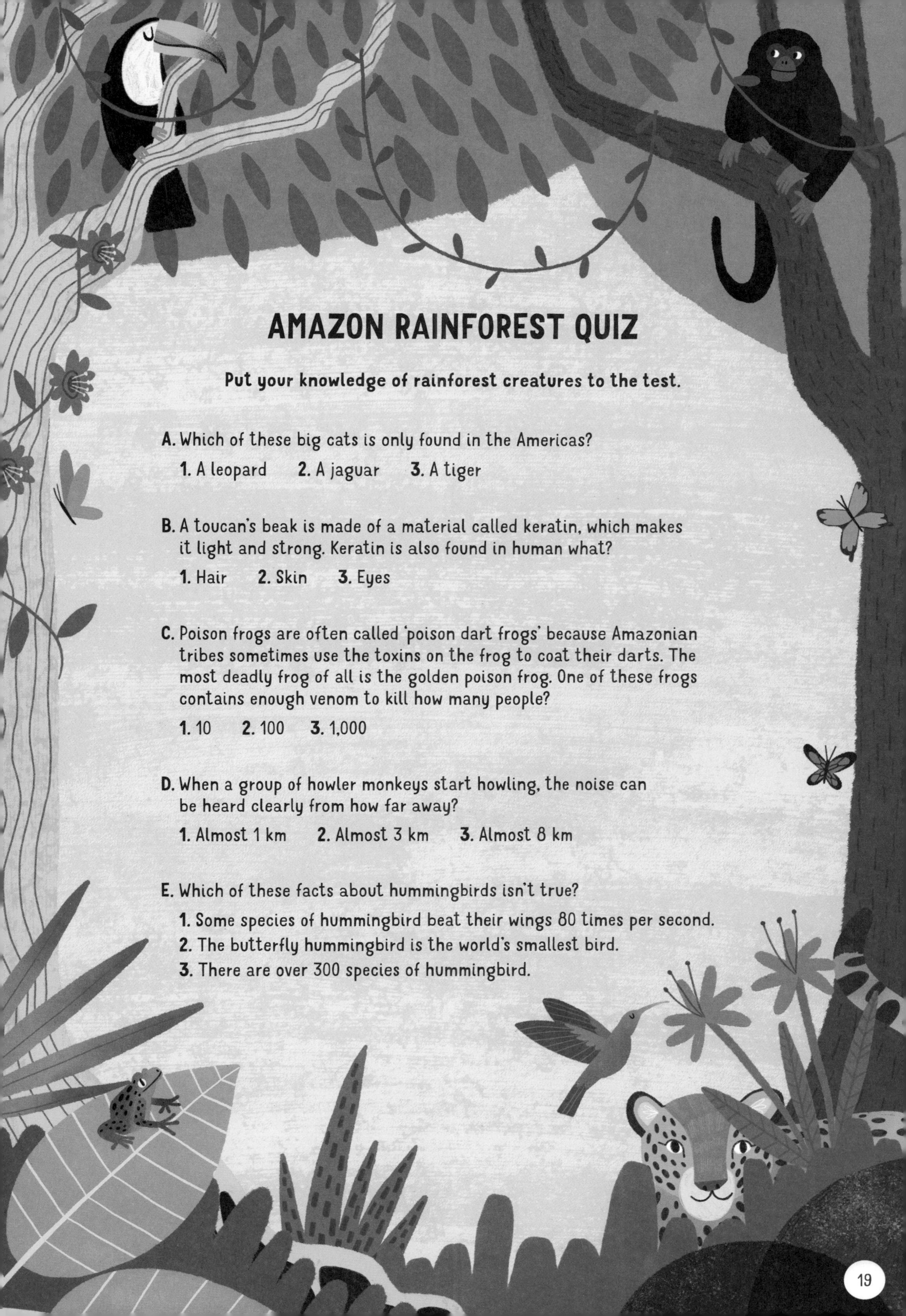

AMAZON RAINFOREST QUIZ

Put your knowledge of rainforest creatures to the test.

A. Which of these big cats is only found in the Americas?

1. A leopard **2.** A jaguar **3.** A tiger

B. A toucan's beak is made of a material called keratin, which makes it light and strong. Keratin is also found in human what?

1. Hair **2.** Skin **3.** Eyes

C. Poison frogs are often called 'poison dart frogs' because Amazonian tribes sometimes use the toxins on the frog to coat their darts. The most deadly frog of all is the golden poison frog. One of these frogs contains enough venom to kill how many people?

1. 10 **2.** 100 **3.** 1,000

D. When a group of howler monkeys start howling, the noise can be heard clearly from how far away?

1. Almost 1 km **2.** Almost 3 km **3.** Almost 8 km

E. Which of these facts about hummingbirds isn't true?

1. Some species of hummingbird beat their wings 80 times per second.
2. The butterfly hummingbird is the world's smallest bird.
3. There are over 300 species of hummingbird.

SNOW LEOPARD SEARCH

Can you spot the snow leopard hidden in this scene?

Snow leopards are found in the cold, rocky mountains of Central Asia. Their light, white-grey fur and dark spots allow them to blend in among the snow and stones perfectly. This has earned them the nickname 'the ghost of the mountains'.

There are as few as 4,000 snow leopards left in the wild.

These cats are built for climbing over treacherous terrain. Their long tails help them to balance and their powerful back legs allow them to leap between rocks with ease.

YAK TRAIL

Help this wild yak and her calf find a trail up to the top of the mountain by stepping only on touching stones that are pentagons. The first stone has been highlighted for you.

Wild yaks are the ancestors of the domestic yak. Only a small number of wild yaks now exist in isolated parts of Central Asia. They are larger and hairier than their domesticated relatives.

Wild yaks are grazing animals and they mainly eat grasses, mosses, herbs and shrubs. Females with young calves will often choose high, steep slopes to graze on, to protect their babies from predators.

WOODLAND JIGSAW

Which of the puzzle pieces below will complete this woodland scene?

Red foxes have 20 different types of call, including various growls, howls and yaps.

Badgers are expert diggers and create complex underground burrows called setts. Some badger setts can be over 100 years old and will have been extended and modified by generations of badgers.

A.

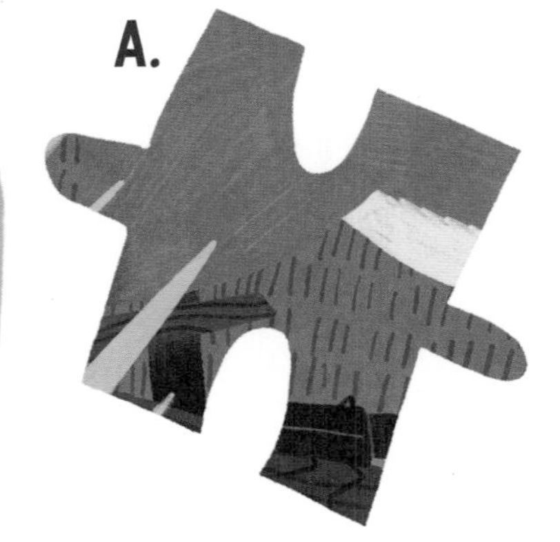

B.

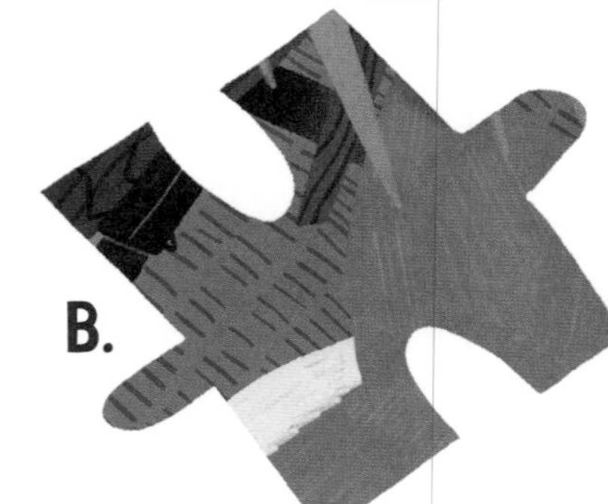

C.

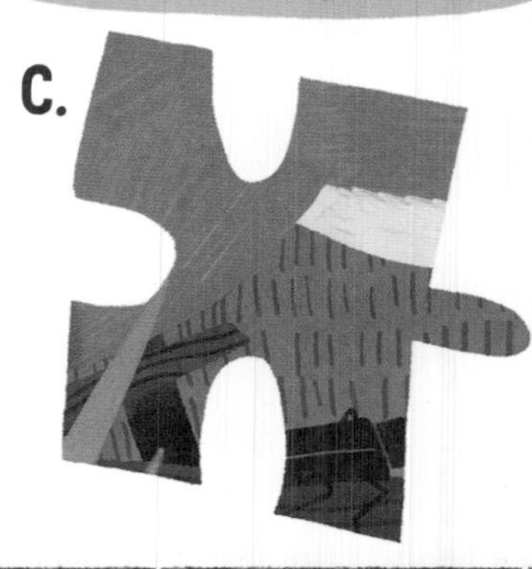

D.

E.

MARTEN MAZE

Help this pine marten climb down the tree to reach its family by following the light brown trail on the trunk.

START

As their name suggests, pine martens spend most of their time in pine trees – they're great climbers! They are omnivores, so eat birds' eggs, small mammals and insects, as well as fungi, berries and fruit.

Pine martens are members of the mustelidae family, which includes weasels, ferrets, otters and badgers.

FINISH

Pine martens are found throughout European woodlands but they are shy animals and hard to spot. In the UK, pine martens are a protected species.

MIGRATION MAZE

Can you help these zebras find a safe route across the river, avoiding the crocodiles and other obstacles?

One of the largest migrations takes place between the Serengeti National Park in Tanzania and the Maasai Mara National Reserve in Kenya. Around 1.5 million animals undertake the journey.

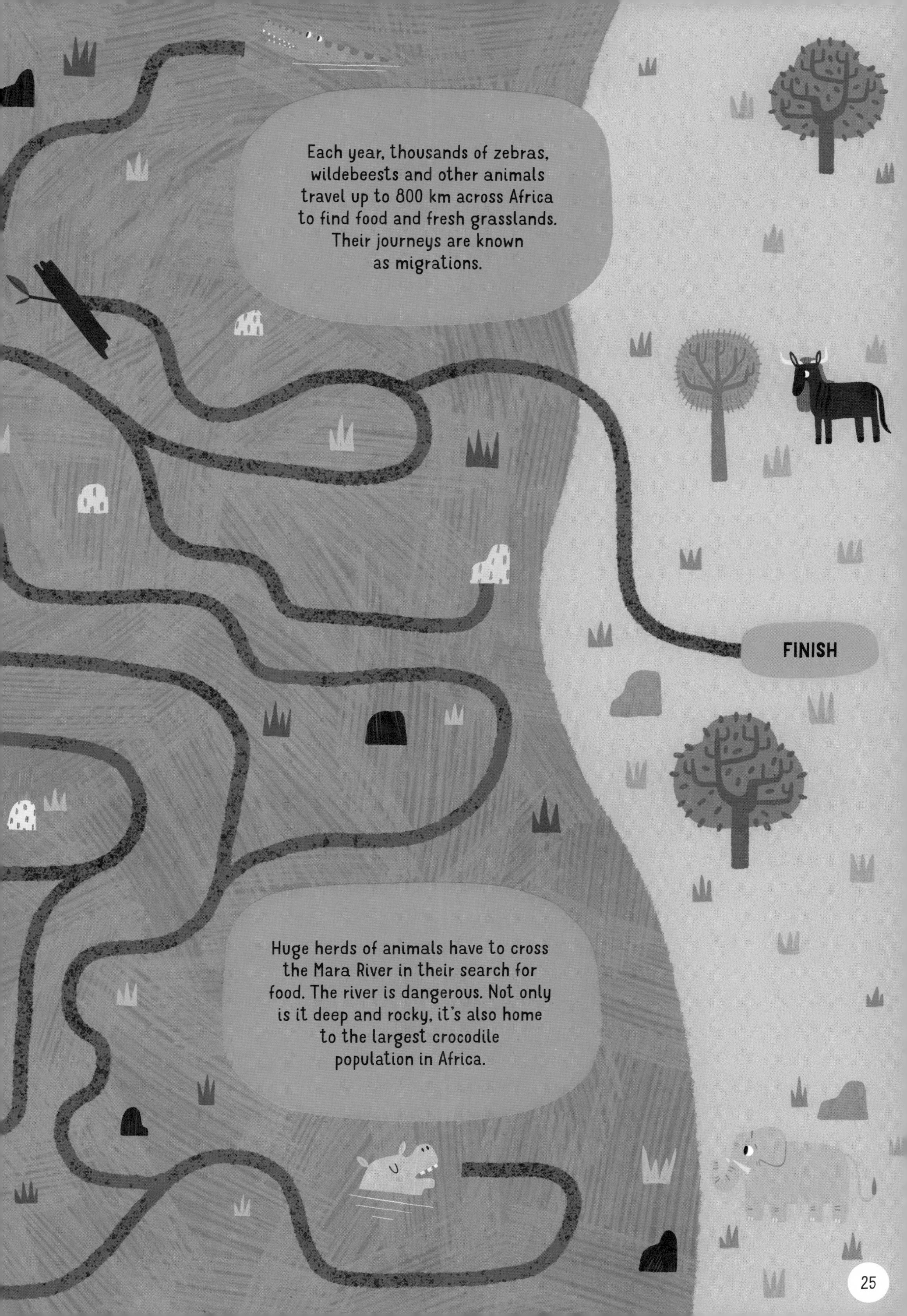
Each year, thousands of zebras, wildebeests and other animals travel up to 800 km across Africa to find food and fresh grasslands. Their journeys are known as migrations.
FINISH
Huge herds of animals have to cross the Mara River in their search for food. The river is dangerous. Not only is it deep and rocky, it's also home to the largest crocodile population in Africa.

BLACK BEAR SUMS

Solve the sums to find out which of these black bear cubs has climbed its tree in the fastest time.

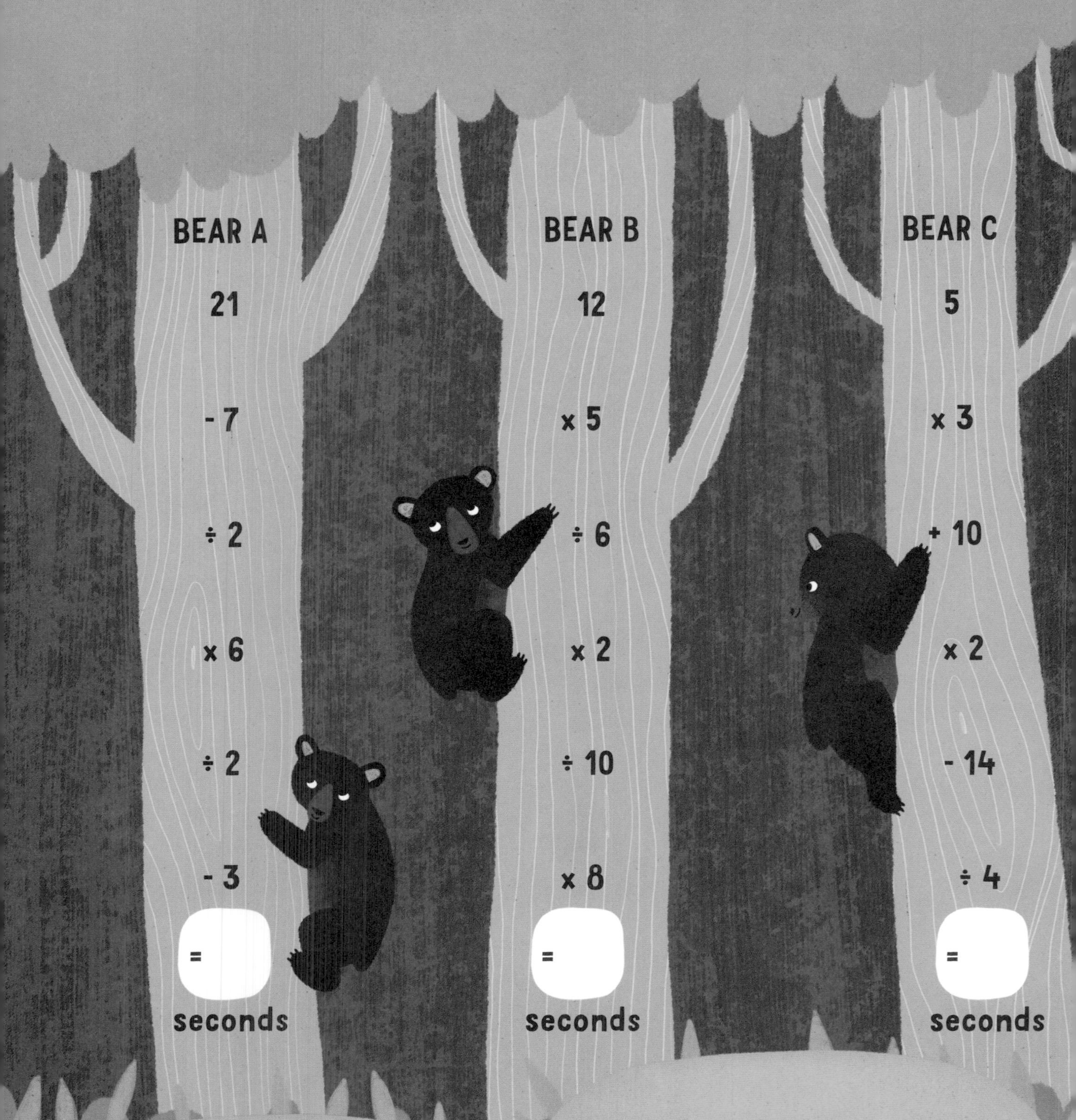

Black bears are the smallest bears found in North America. They live in densely forested areas and eat a mix of fruits, nuts, vegetation and, occasionally, fish.

They have short claws, which make them excellent tree-climbers – an adult black bear can scale a 30-m tree in about 30 seconds. Mother bears will teach their cubs how to climb as soon as they leave the den. Then, if a predator is close by, the young bears can scamper up a tree to safety.

COUGAR CO-ORDINATES

Here is a map of this cougar's territory. Use the co-ordinates to find out the cougar's favourite spots and the order in which he will visit them during the day.

1. Where does the cougar's day start at A,2? ....

2. What does he have to cross at B,1? ....

3. What does he head to at E,4? ....

4. The cougar meets which animal at F,6? ....

5. What will he rest on at C,7? ....

Unlike tigers, lions, leopards and jaguars, cougars cannot roar. They are built like smaller cats, so their vocal cords can only make a deep purring noise.

Cougars are some of the most adaptable big cats on the planet. They are found throughout the Americas – from Canada to Patagonia – and in almost every kind of habitat, including forests, deserts and cities.

ODD SHARK OUT

Grey nurse sharks are often found in large groups in the seas around Australia. All of the sharks below are grey nurse sharks – apart from one. Can you spot it?

Grey nurse sharks are also found in the southern Atlantic and off the coast of southern Africa. Although they are big and look quite scary, grey nurse sharks are fairly calm creatures and don't usually pose a threat to humans.

Unlike fish, which have a gas-filled bladder to help them float, sharks must swim constantly to stop them from sinking in the water. Grey nurse sharks will also take gulps of air from the surface and store it in their stomach to allow them to hover in the water.

SPOT THE SEA DRAGONS

This patch of seaweed is full of leafy sea dragons.
How many can you find?

These camouflaged creatures are found in the waters off southern and eastern Australia. Their plant-like bodies help them to blend in perfectly with the algae and seagrasses that they live among.

Male leafy sea dragons carry and give birth to their young, like male seahorses do. Unlike seahorses, which carry their eggs in a pouch, sea dragons carry their eggs in a special patch under their tail until they hatch.

POLAR STEPPING STONES

Guide the polar bear from one side of the ice to the other. Step only on pieces of ice that contain multiples of 3 and are next to each other.

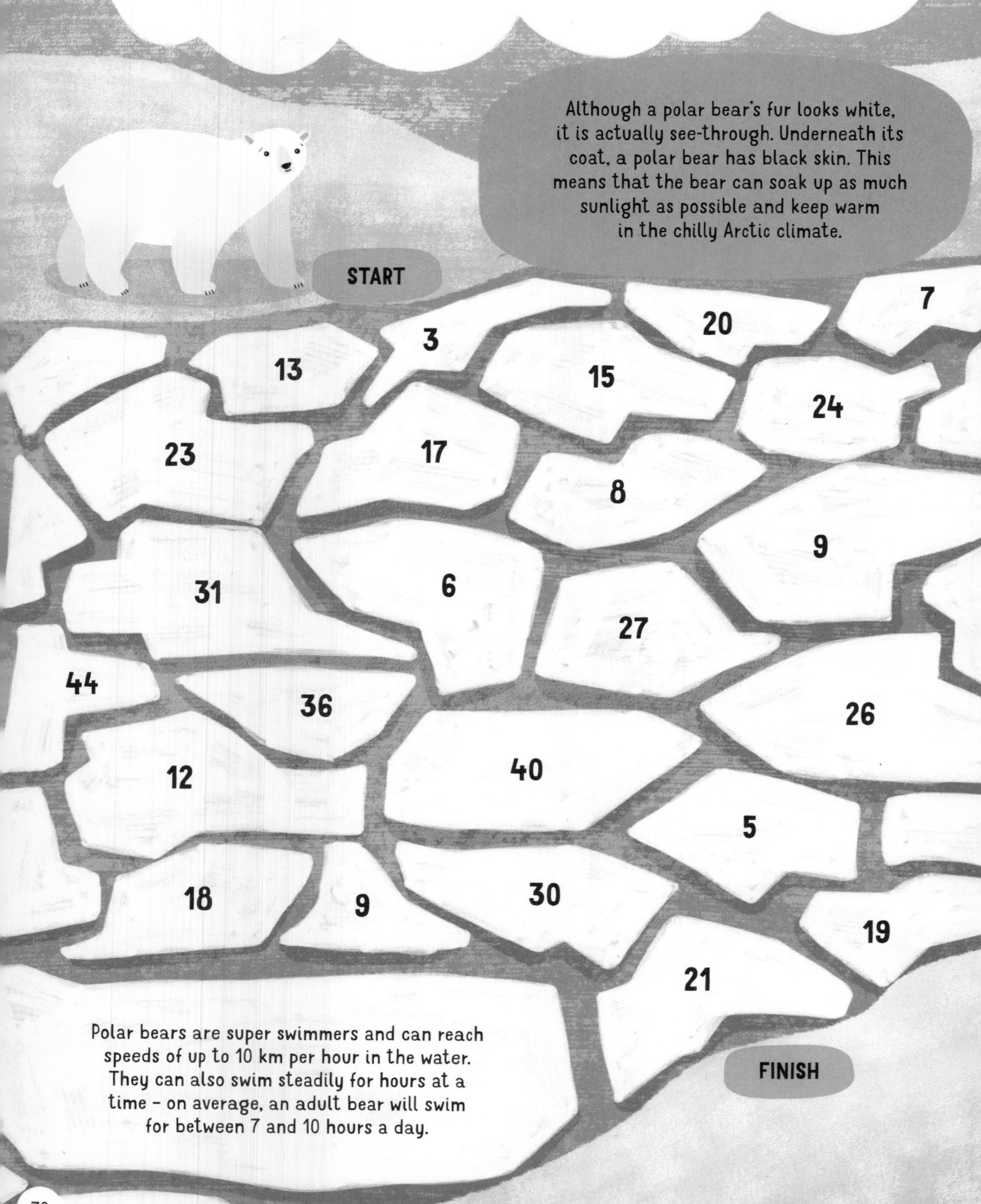

SNOWY OWL SPOT THE DIFFERENCE

Can you spot ten differences between these two pictures of a snowy owl and her chicks?

One of the largest owls in the world, snowy owls are tough and can survive temperatures as low as -40°C.

Snowy owls build their nests on the ground and lay between 3 and 11 eggs. Both parents care for the young and will fiercely defend their chicks against predators.

ANTEATER MAZE
Find the one route through this anthill that will allow the anteater to slurp up all of the black ants. Avoid the red ants, though – they'll bite!
FINISH
Anteaters have no teeth. Instead, they rely on their long tongues to lick up ants and termites. A giant anteater's tongue can be up to 60 cm long and one giant anteater can eat up to 35,000 ants a day.
An anteater has to eat ants quickly to avoid painful bites. It flicks its tongue up to 160 times a minute to try to eat as many ants as possible.

ANT TRAIL

Follow the ants in the order shown on the leaf to get from start to finish. You can move across, up and down but not diagonally.

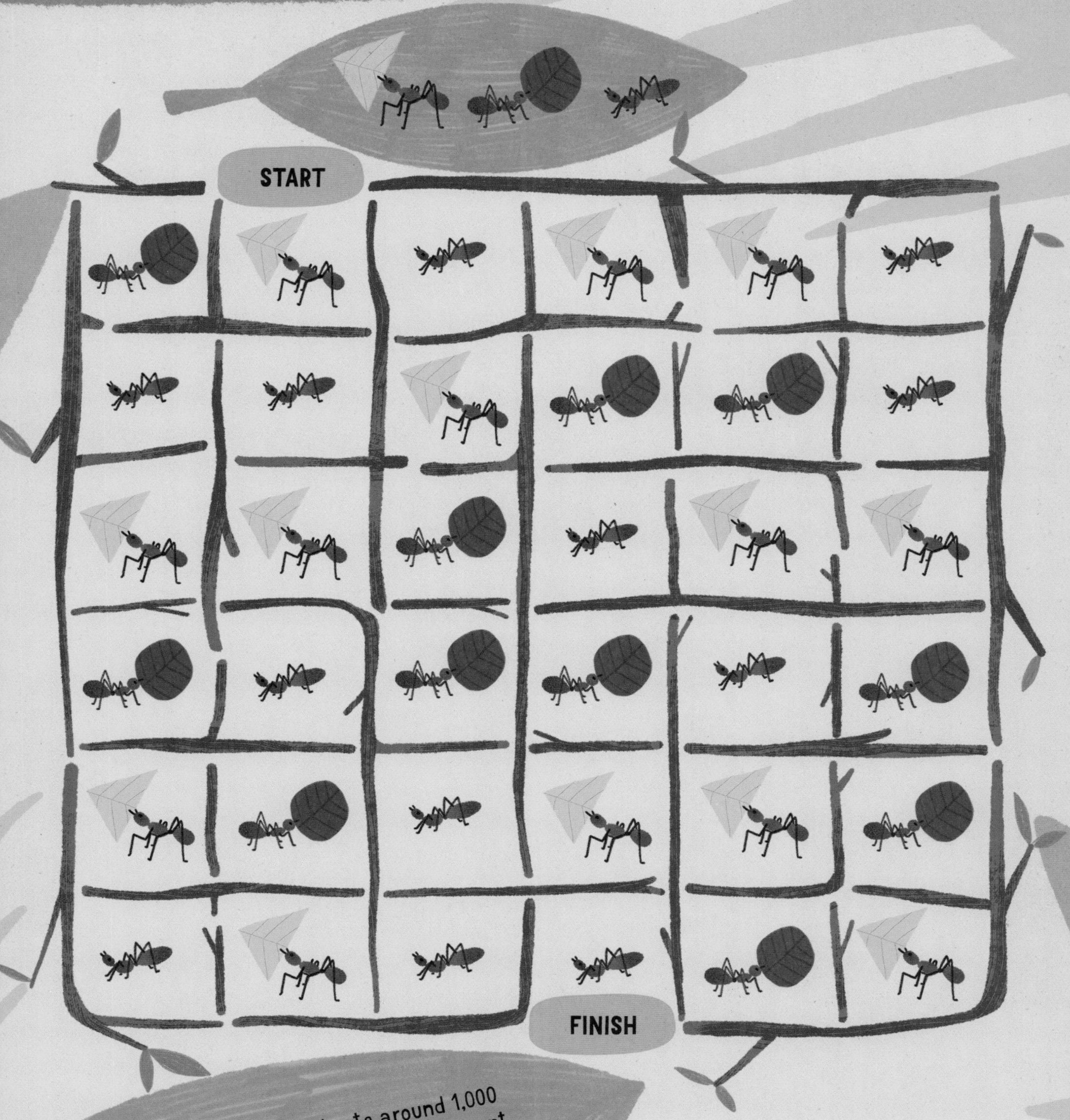

A leafcutter ant's jaws vibrate around 1,000 times a second as it chops up a leaf. The ant then carries the piece of leaf back to its nest. There it is used to grow a special kind of fungus, which the ants feed on.

As ants carry the leaf cuttings back to their nest, they usually form a long, single-file line. These lines can stretch for up to 30 m.

BORNEO SEARCH AND FIND

The island of Borneo in Southeast Asia is home to an incredible range of wildlife. Several of these animals are not found anywhere else in the world. Can you spot the rare creatures in the key in this scene? Some appear more than once.

Orangutans live in rainforests on the islands of Sumatra and Borneo. The orangutans on the two islands are separate species and look slightly different from one another – Bornean orangutans have darker fur and broader faces. Both species are threatened by deforestation.

Proboscis monkeys only live in Borneo and are named after the long, bulbous noses that the males develop ('proboscis' means nose). They are the best swimmers of all primates and have webbed feet.

KEY
BORNEAN ORANGUTAN
BORNEO PYGMY ELEPHANT
SUNDA CLOUDED LEOPARD
FALSE GHARIAL
WALLACE'S FLYING FROG
SLOW LORIS
GREAT HORNBILL
SPINY TERRAPIN
BORNEO SHORT-TAILED PYTHON
PROBOSCIS MONKEY

PORCUPINE SILHOUETTE

Which of these silhouettes matches this African crested porcupine?

There are 29 species of porcupine in the world. The largest is the African crested porcupine.

A porcupine's quills usually sit flat against its body but it will raise them to scare predators if it feels threatened. The quills on an African crested porcupine can be up to 30 cm long.

AFRICAN ELEPHANT MEMORY GAME

They say that an elephant never forgets ... but how do you measure up? Study the elephant family on this page carefully, then turn the page to see how much you can remember about the scene.

An African elephant's brain is the largest of any land animal – it can weigh up to 5.4 kg.

Elephants live in big family groups and maintain close relationships with each other throughout their lives.

An elephant's memory is key to its survival. Older female elephants are in charge of taking their herd to sources of food and water. They can remember routes that they went on long ago, which can save the herd if their usual food sources run out.

AFRICAN ELEPHANT MEMORY GAME

Once you've studied the picture on the previous page, answer the questions below.

1. How many butterflies are there in the picture? How many are red and how many are pink?

   ....

2. What is one elephant holding in its trunk?

   ....

3. What is sitting on the elephant's back, and what colour is it?

   ....

4. How many elephants are squirting water with their trunks?

   ....

5. As well as butterflies, what other insect can you see in the picture?

   ....

6. How many birds are flying, and what colour are they?

   ....

MEERKAT SEQUENCES

Look carefully at the sequences below. Can you work out which meerkats are missing from each sequence?

A. ?   ?

B. ?   ?

C. ?   ?

The venom of a snake or scorpion doesn't hurt a meerkat. In fact, these little creatures will happily eat poisonous creepy-crawlies and reptiles for dinner.

Although meerkats are tough, they'd still make a tasty meal for birds of prey or jackals. To protect one another, meerkats live in big groups called 'mobs'. The meerkats take it in turns to act as a look-out, scanning the desert for predators. They send out a warning call if they spot danger.

TANGLED TRAILS
Which pawprint trail leads to the Canadian lynx?
Canadian lynx live in the forests of North America and have thick fur that keeps them warm throughout the freezing cold winters. Their large, wide paws act a bit like snowshoes, allowing the lynx to run over the snow easily in pursuit of their favourite prey – snowshoe hares.
Snowshoe hares form such an important part of a Canadian lynx's diet that when their population dips so does that of the lynx.
A.
B.
C.

BEAVER BRAIN-TEASER

Use the following clues to work out which tree this beaver is going to cut down for its dam. The beaver wants a tree that has ...

1. A narrow trunk
2. Round leaves
3. Smooth bark

Beavers have large front teeth that never stop growing. The teeth have a natural protective coating that contains iron. This keeps them strong and also gives them an orange colour.

To keep their teeth short, beavers must constantly chew wood and trees, which they use for food and to build their homes. Beavers particularly like willow, aspen, cherry and birch trees.

AUSTRALIAN ANIMAL MIX-UP

There are some incredible facts about Australian animals on this page, but they are all placed next to the wrong creatures. Can you work out which fact belongs with which animal?

FLYING FOX

A. Another name for this animal is the 'long-nosed bandicoot'.

BILBY

B. A marsupial that has cube-shaped poo.

TASMANIAN DEVIL

D. The biggest carnivorous mammal in Australia.

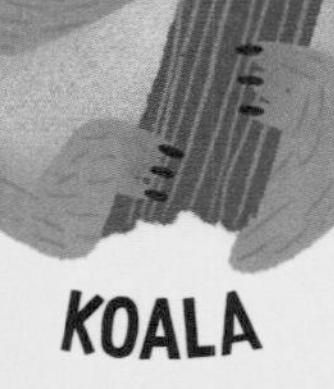

C. These animals help to pollinate trees, much in the way bees do.

KOALA

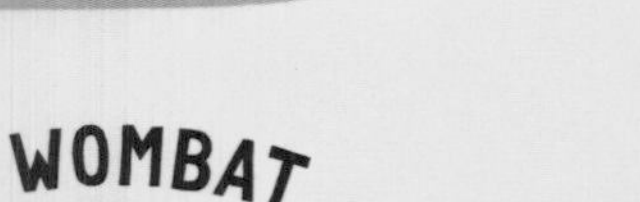

DINGO

F. A marsupial that comes out at night and carries up to four babies in its pouch.

WOMBAT

E. A marsupial that eats only eucalyptus leaves.

BIRD IN THE BUSH

Join up the dots to complete this picture of a noisy bird who lives in the Australian bush. Do you know what it's called?

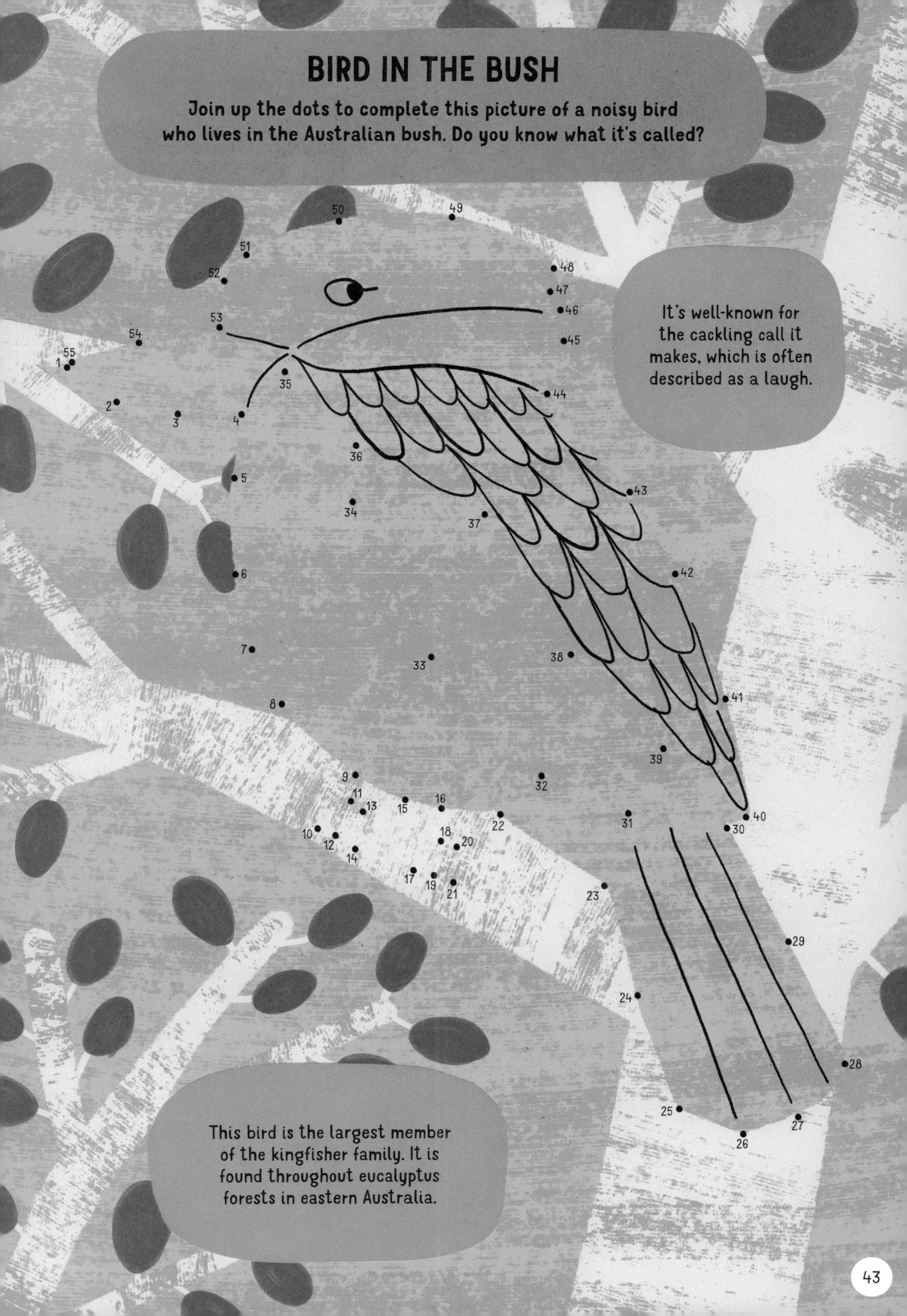

It's well-known for the cackling call it makes, which is often described as a laugh.

This bird is the largest member of the kingfisher family. It is found throughout eucalyptus forests in eastern Australia.

MONKEY PUZZLE

Can you spot ten differences between these pictures of Japanese macaques having a hot bath?

Also known as snow monkeys, these macaques live in Japan's forests and mountains. Apart from humans, they are the only primates that live this far north in the world. The monkeys gather together in large groups during winter to keep one another warm.

The Japanese macaques that live in Jigokudani Monkey Park enjoy bathing in hot springs. As well as warming them up, some scientists think that the water helps reduce stress among the monkeys.

DANCE PARTNERS

These red-crowned cranes have assembled for their courtship dances, but all the partners have got mixed up. Reunite the pairs by matching each crane with its mirror-image twin.

Red-crowned cranes are one of the largest and rarest species of crane in the world.

These birds mate for life. To establish or re-establish a bond, a pair of cranes will take part in an elaborate courtship dance, which includes bows, head bops and leaps.

JUNGLE RUN

Follow the paths to find out which of these Amazon mammals is on the right track for the watering hole. What creatures do each of the animals meet on their travels?

JAGUAR

Jaguars are the largest cat in the Americas and the third largest big cat species (after tigers and lions) in the world.

Giant armadillos are found in grasslands, woodlands and rainforests in South America. These creatures have more teeth than any other land mammal – an adult giant armadillo can have up to 100 teeth in its mouth.

ARMADILLO

COATI

To hide from predators, a tapir can submerge itself underwater, using its nose like a snorkel.

FINISH

TAPIR

SHY GUY

Complete this dot-to-dot to reveal a shy creature that lives in the mountains of Nepal, China and Myanmar. Do you know what it is?

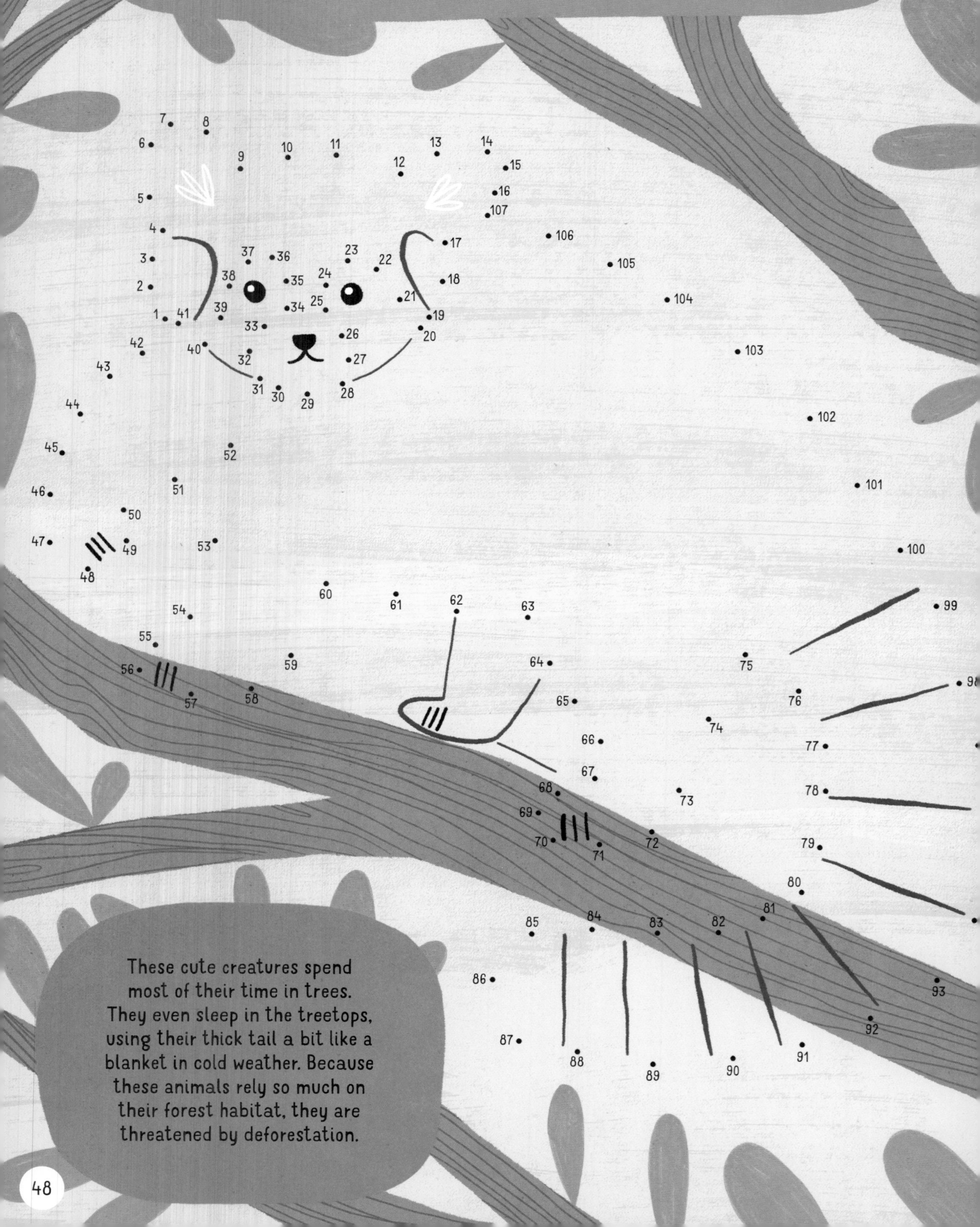

These cute creatures spend most of their time in trees. They even sleep in the treetops, using their thick tail a bit like a blanket in cold weather. Because these animals rely so much on their forest habitat, they are threatened by deforestation.

TIGER TERRITORIES

These four Siberian tigers are searching for a territory of their own. Can you divide the page into four separate territories, using just three straight lines? Each territory must contain a tiger, a lake and a forest.

Siberian tigers are the largest species of big cat and live in remote forests in Russia, China and North Korea. Because these tigers live in harsh environments, they have to roam great distances to find food and have large territories as a result. A male tiger's territory can be up to 2,000 km^2, though it will usually overlap with several female tigers' territories.

NEST MUDDLE

Sociable weaver birds live in Southern Africa and work in teams to build the largest nests in the world. Follow the paths to guide each bird to its chicks in this mega nest.

Rather than building a nest in their pairs, groups of sociable weaver birds work together to build a giant nest that can house their entire colony, a bit like a beehive or a block of flats. Each pair then raises their chicks in their own nest chamber.

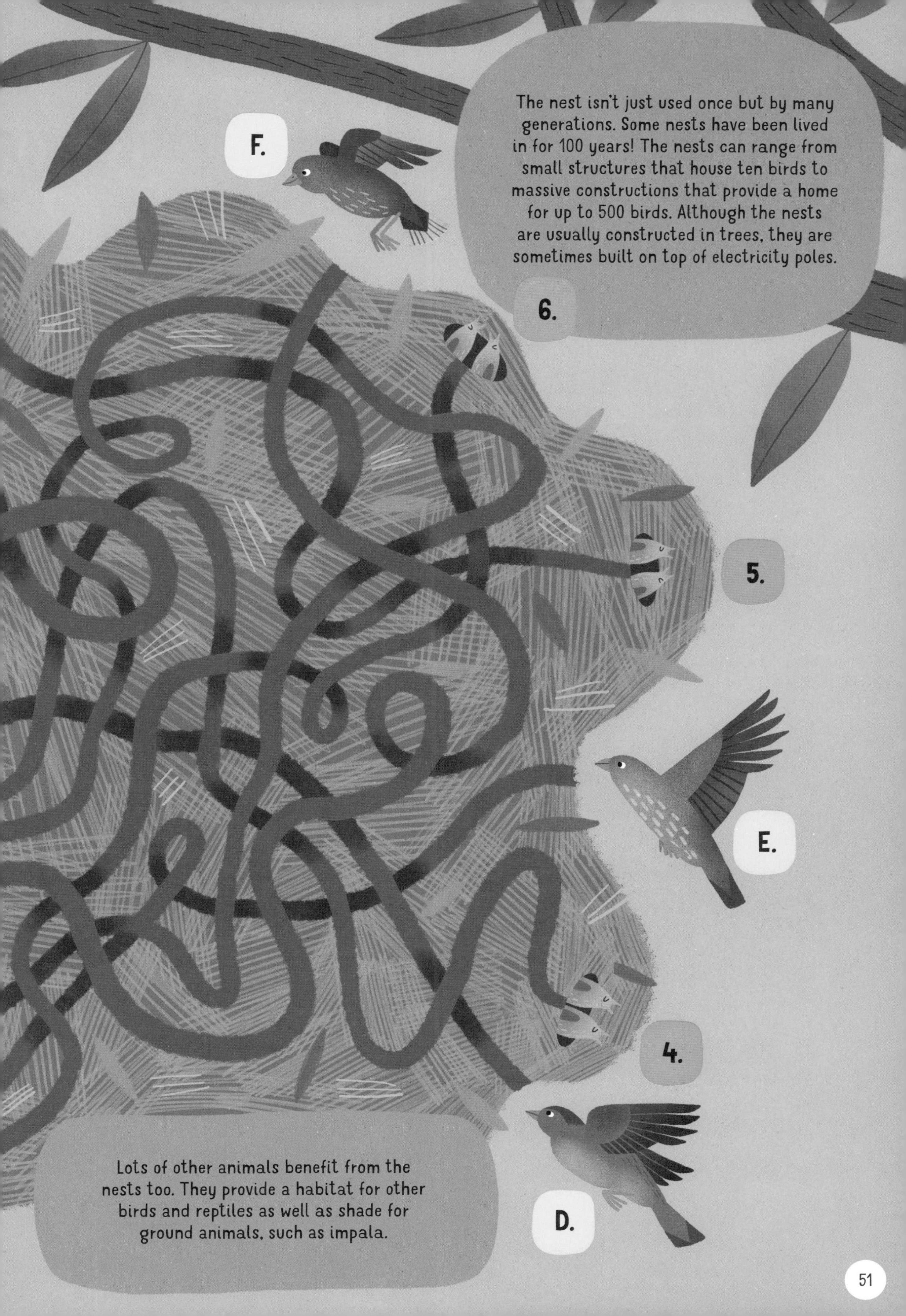

The nest isn't just used once but by many generations. Some nests have been lived in for 100 years! The nests can range from small structures that house ten birds to massive constructions that provide a home for up to 500 birds. Although the nests are usually constructed in trees, they are sometimes built on top of electricity poles.

Lots of other animals benefit from the nests too. They provide a habitat for other birds and reptiles as well as shade for ground animals, such as impala.

POND PUZZLER
There are two different species of duck on this pond – mallard ducks and tufted ducks. The mallard ducks have yellow and brown ducklings and the tufted ducks have dark brown ducklings. If each pair of mallard ducks has six ducklings and each pair of tufted ducks has four ducklings, how many ducklings in total are missing from the picture?
KEY
TUFTED DUCKS
MALLARD DUCKS
The mallard duck is thought to be the most common and widespread duck on Earth. It is found across Asia, Europe and North America. There are believed to be 10 million mallards in the USA alone.
Tufted ducks usually feed by diving and can dive as deep as 15 m in search of food. Freshwater mussels are among their favourite things to eat. They also forage for insects, seeds and aquatic plants.

BEE BRAIN-TEASER

This meadow is full of busy bees. Can you find the following groups in the patch of wildflowers below?

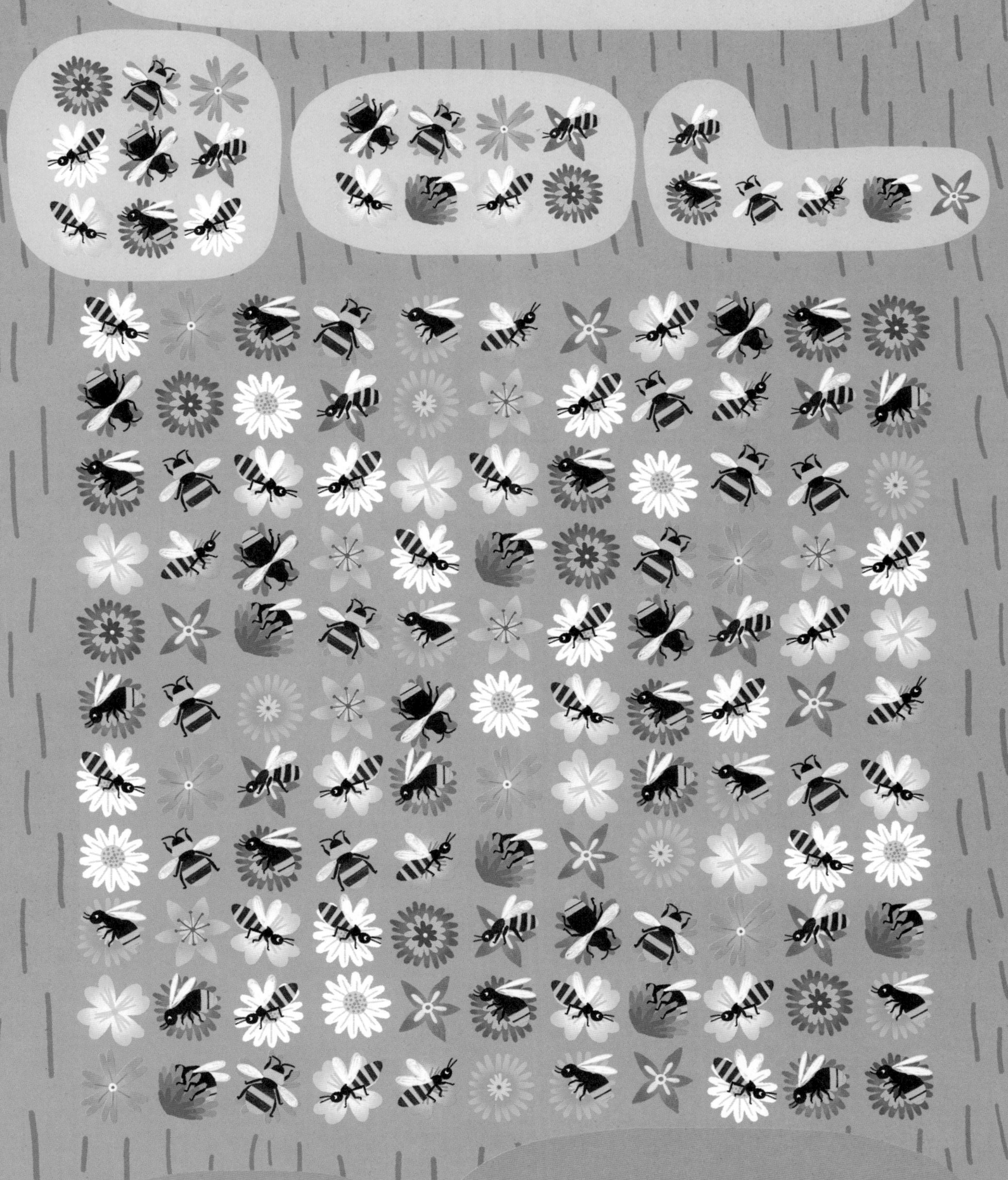

There are 250 species of bee in the UK alone – and around 20,000 species of bee on Earth.

Bees pick up pollen on their legs and bodies as they fly from flower to flower searching for nectar to eat. Pollen needs to be taken from one flower to another in order for plants to reproduce. A honeybee may visit between 50 and 100 flowers in a single trip.

TWIT T-WHO?

Can you match the back-to-front silhouettes to the correct North American owl?

Like many owls, the great grey owl has a round 'disc' of feathers on its face. It uses this a bit like a satellite dish to pick up noises and track its prey. Because the great grey has such a large disc, it can hear sounds over 95 m away.

Some owls, such as the long-eared owl, the western screech owl and the great horned owl, have 'ear tufts' on their heads. These aren't actually ears but bunches of feathers. Scientists think owls may use them to communicate with one another or as a kind of camouflage.

COUNT THE BISON

How many bison and their calves can you count in this herd? And how many moose can you find hiding among them?

Tens of millions of wild bison once roamed across the plains of North America. During the 19th century so many were killed for food and sport that only around 1,000 remained by the late 1880s. Conservation efforts have saved the species, but most of the half a million bison alive today live in captivity.

Moose are the largest species of deer. An adult male can weigh up to 580 kg and have antlers that span almost 2 m from one end to the other. Although they're big animals, moose can run at speeds of up to 56 km per hour and are also good swimmers.

ROCK POOL SPOT THE DIFFERENCE

Can you spot 20 differences between these two rock pool pictures?

Found along seashores, rock pools are home to some incredibly tough creatures. Animals that live in a rock pool have to be able to cope with an environment that is constantly changing. Their pool is flooded with seawater when the tide (the level of the sea) comes in and is exposed to the sun and predators when the tide goes out.

This pool contains creatures found in European rock pools, such as mussels, limpets, sea anemones, common starfish, shore crabs, common prawns and blenny fish. Many of these animals are adapted to survive difficult conditions. When the tide goes out, sea anemones, for example, close up to stop themselves from drying out.

Limpets have tiny teeth which they use to rake up algae from the surface of rocks. Incredibly, limpet teeth are the strongest natural material in the world. Scientists think the structure of limpet teeth could be copied to build planes and cars in the future.

INDIAN ANIMALS: TRUE OR FALSE?

Put your knowledge of Indian wildlife to the test. Which of the following facts are true and which are false?

1. A Bengal tiger's stripes act a bit like human fingerprints – each pattern is unique to each individual cat.
2. There are thought to be 10,000 Bengal tigers left in the wild.
3. Indian rhinos avoid water and spend most of their time in dry, arid environments.
4. Hanuman langur monkeys are considered sacred by Hindus and wild troops are traditionally fed on Tuesdays and Saturdays in the city of New Delhi.
5. Growing up to 5.5 m, the king cobra is the longest venomous snake in the world.
6. Like other bears, sloth bears hibernate in caves.
7. Leopards can jump up to 6 m in one leap.
8. The Asian elephant is much larger than the African elephant.
9. Nearly all lions live in Africa, but a small population of Asiatic lions survive in a forest in western India. These lions are slightly smaller than African lions.
10. The Indian star tortoise has a very curved and bumpy shell. This means it can easily get back on its feet if it is tipped on to its back.

PEACOCK PUZZLER

Can you find the following pieces in the peacock picture below? Write the co-ordinates underneath each piece.

Peafowls are native to India – the male birds ('peacocks') are easily recognized by their beautiful green and blue tail feathers. The females ('peahens') are brown and have short tails. Peacocks use their stunning tail feathers to attract peahens.

A peacock's tail can grow to 1.5 m long and contains around 200 feathers. At the top of each feather is a round 'eyespot'. Tiny fibres in these spots catch the light and make it look like they are moving.

REINDEER TRAILS

By completing these maths sequences, can you work out which reindeer travels the furthest to reach the tasty lichen?

Reindeer have hollowed out hooves, which they use to scoop out snow in search of food. They survive winter months by eating a plant called lichen – this spongy plant can grow underneath the snow because it doesn't need much sunlight. It is packed full of energy to keep the reindeer going.

COUNTING HARES

How many Arctic hares can you spot in this scene?
And how many have still got their brown summer coat?

Arctic hares have a super sense of smell. It helps them to find food hidden under the snow, which they dig up with their long claws. Incredibly, they can also see almost 360° around themselves without turning their heads. This allows them to spot predators, such as lynx, snowy owls and Arctic foxes.

In winter, Arctic hares have thick, white coats. They live on rocky hillsides where there are no trees, so their white fur keeps them hidden from predators in the snow. The white hair is replaced by shorter, brown-grey fur in summer to help them camouflage against their rocky habitat. But their tails always stay white!

BEAR BRUNCH

Spectacled bears are very adaptable and eat lots of different things. How many tasty treats from the key can you spot in this scene? Spectacled bears will search for food in trees as well as on the ground, so keep your eyes peeled.

Also known as Andean bears, spectacled bears are the only species of bear from South America. They are found in a variety of habitats but prefer the dense cloud forests on the slopes of the Andes mountains. These bears were the inspiration behind one of film and literature's most famous bears, Paddington.

VICUÑA JIGSAW

Work out which jigsaw pieces you need to complete the picture of a herd of vicuñas.

Vicuñas are closely related to alpacas and llamas. They live in large herds in alpine regions of the Andes mountains in South America. Females give birth to a single calf, which is able to stand just 15 minutes after it has been born.

BIG LEAPS

Help this tree kangaroo get to the ground by jumping only on branches that contain multiples of four. The branches that you land on must follow the order of the four times table (4, 8 and so on).

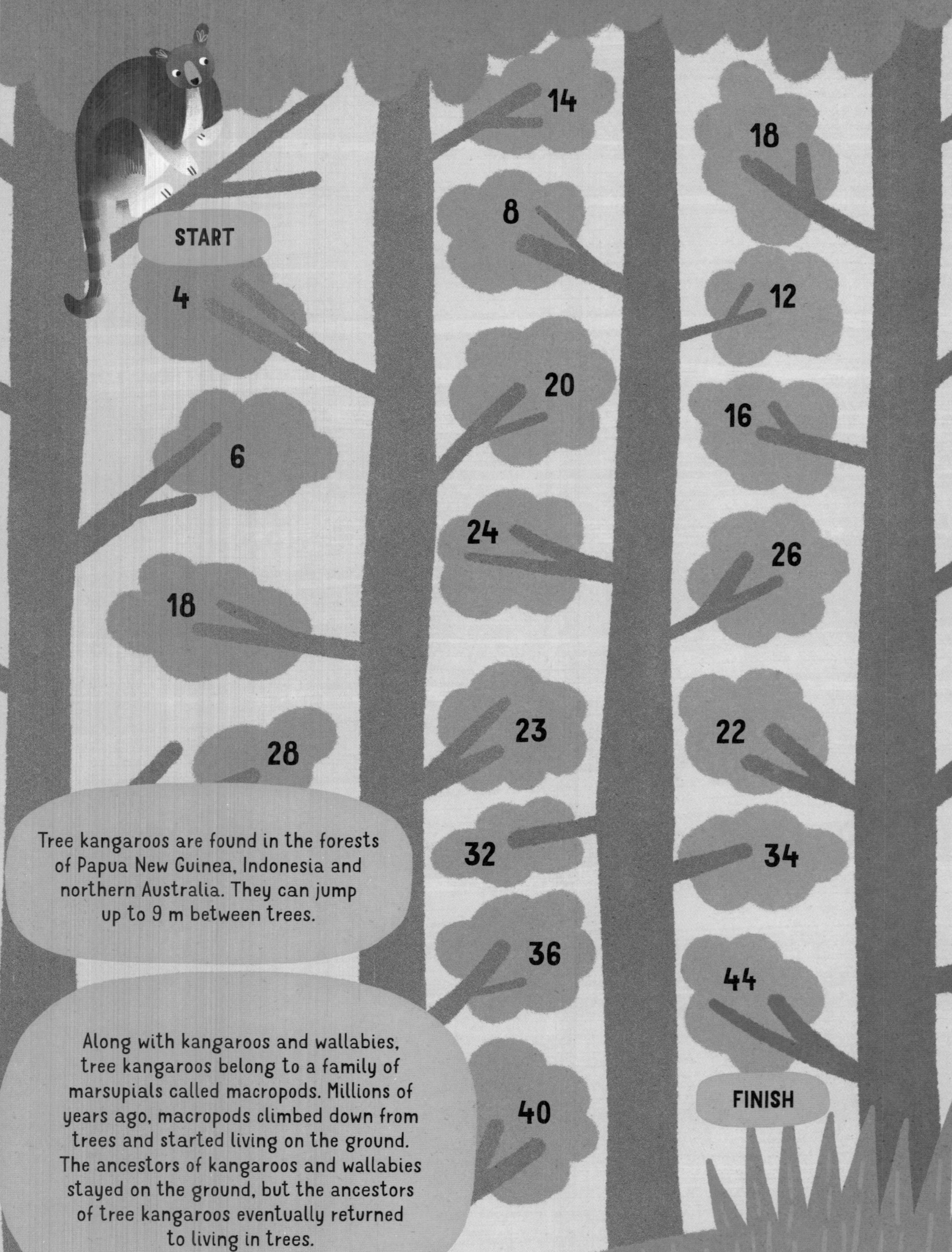

Tree kangaroos are found in the forests of Papua New Guinea, Indonesia and northern Australia. They can jump up to 9 m between trees.

Along with kangaroos and wallabies, tree kangaroos belong to a family of marsupials called macropods. Millions of years ago, macropods climbed down from trees and started living on the ground. The ancestors of kangaroos and wallabies stayed on the ground, but the ancestors of tree kangaroos eventually returned to living in trees.

PERFECT PARTNER

Use the following clues to work out which male bird of paradise this brown female will choose for a mate:

1. His wings are not blue.
2. He has short tail feathers.
3. He has a blue beak.

Birds of paradise live in Papua New Guinea and Australia. There are thought to be around 42 species of these beautiful birds, and each one looks very different to the other. The male birds come in a variety of incredible colours, with stunning tail feathers, plumes, crests, riffs and head fans. The females tend to have plainer feathers.

Males use their elaborate feathers, along with complex calls and dance moves, to attract a mate. Some will put on courtship displays as a group, while others will clear a space on the forest floor to perform for the female. The displays can last for several hours.

MARINE MAZE

Can you find a route to guide this marine iguana down to the green algae and then back up to the surface?

Marine iguanas are the only sea-going lizards in the world and live on the Galápagos Islands in the Pacific Ocean. It's thought that their ancestors drifted out to sea on logs and washed up on the Galápagos. The lizards are normally dark grey, but the males change to red and green colours during the breeding season.

Often seen sunning themselves on rocks near the coast, marine iguanas will swim out to sea and dive below the waves to feed on seaweed and green algae. They can hold their breath underwater for around 30 minutes at a time.

TORTOISE YEARS

Can you complete the number pyramids on these giant tortoises' shells? Each square contains a number that is equal to the sum of the two beneath it. The number at the top of each pyramid tells you the age of that tortoise. Which one is the oldest?

Galápagos tortoises are some of the longest-living animals in the world – the oldest on record was 152 years old. It's possible that there might be tortoises alive on the islands today that were there when Charles Darwin visited in 1835.

The Galápagos Islands are named after their tortoises. When the islands were discovered by Spanish sailors in the 1500s, they named them 'galápago', which is Spanish for 'tortoise'.

ALBATROSS JOURNEYS

This picture shows the fishing trips that two albatross parents make in a week to feed their chick. One parent always collects green fish and the other always collects blue fish. By adding up the numbers next to all the green fish and then adding up all the numbers next to all the blue fish, can you work out which parent has collected the most?

The wandering albatross has the largest wingspan of any bird in the world – its wings can stretch a whopping 3.5 m across. This allows the bird to glide through the sky without flapping its wings for several hours at a time. Albatrosses have been known to fly 16,000 km in a single journey.

Wandering albatross pairs stay together for life – which can be as long as 50 years. They raise one chick every two years. An albatross chick will eat up to 100 kg of food before it is ready to fend for itself, so the parents are constantly flying out to sea on long foraging trips.

FOLLOW THE KRILL

Help the blue whale munch its way through this patch of tasty krill, following the krill in the order below. You can move across, up and down but not diagonally.

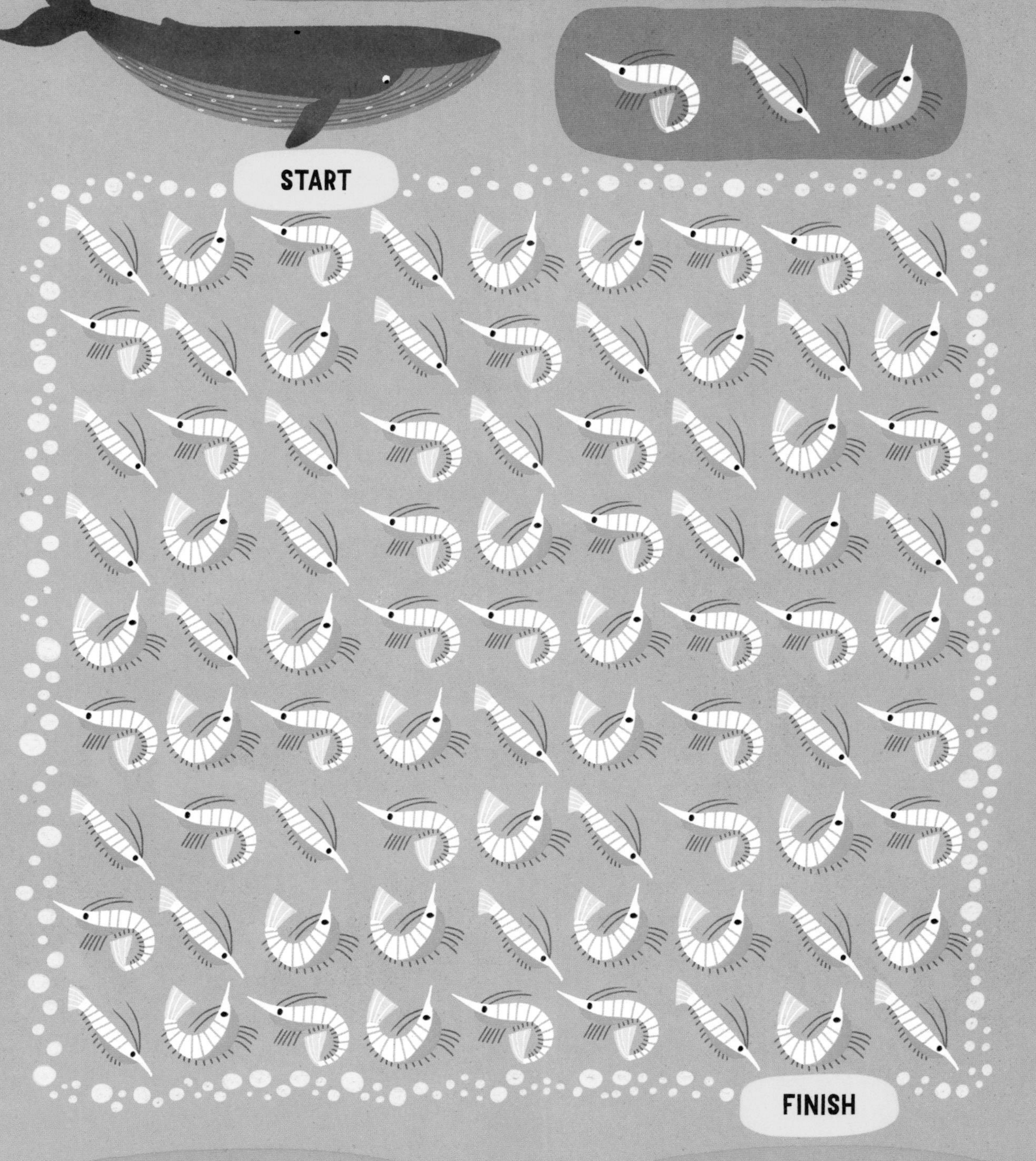

Krill are small, shrimp-like creatures, each one about the size of a paper clip. Hundreds of marine animals – from the blue whale to the Adélie penguin – rely on krill as their food source. In fact, the entire Antarctic ecosystem would collapse without these tiny shellfish.

The blue whale is the largest animal ever known to have lived on Earth. It's also the loudest – blue whales communicate with each other through a series of cries, which can be louder than a jet engine. They have big appetites to match: during summer, a blue whale can eat up to 40 million krill in a single day.

FIND THE FISH

Can you find the clownfish living in the sea anemones? The numbers around the edge of the grid tell you how many fish appear in each row and column. A fish can only be found horizontally or vertically next to an anemone. Fish are never next to each other, neither vertically, horizontally nor diagonally. Look at the example on the right to see how the puzzle works.

EXAMPLE:

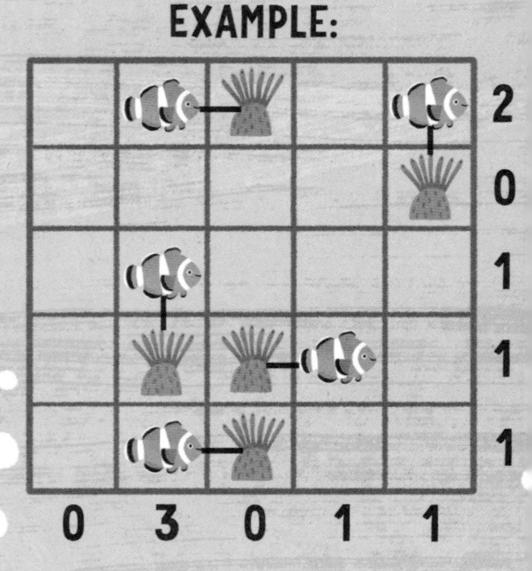

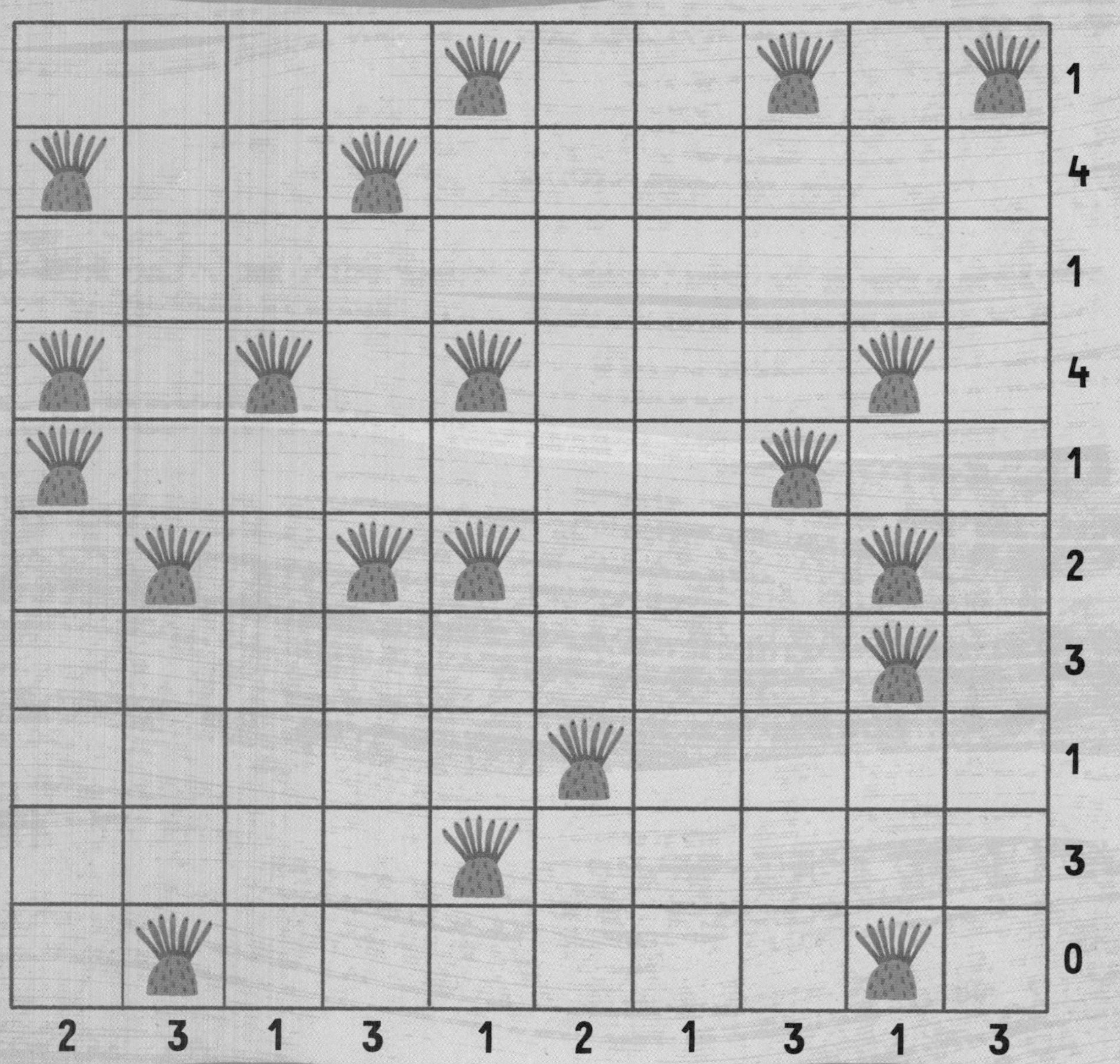

Clownfish and sea anemones have a very special relationship. A clownfish will live among the tentacles of its chosen anemone for its entire life. A special layer of mucus on the clownfish protects it from the anemone's toxic sting.

The anemone's stinging tentacles shield the clownfish from predators, while the clownfish chases away other fish who want to eat the anemone. It also keeps the anemone clean by picking off parasites.

DUGONG DINNER

This dugong munches her way through eight seagrass plants every 30 minutes. How long will it take her to eat all of the seagrass plants in this meadow?

Dugongs are large marine mammals. They are related to manatees and elephants.

Dugongs are vegetarians and spend most of their time munching on seagrass in the warm waters of the Indian and Pacific Oceans. Seagrass is not only vital for dugongs – 50 per cent of the world's fisheries and the livelihoods of 3 billion people living in coastal communities depend on this plant.

SAIGA SILHOUETTES

Study these silhouettes to work out which one matches this strange-looking saiga antelope exactly.

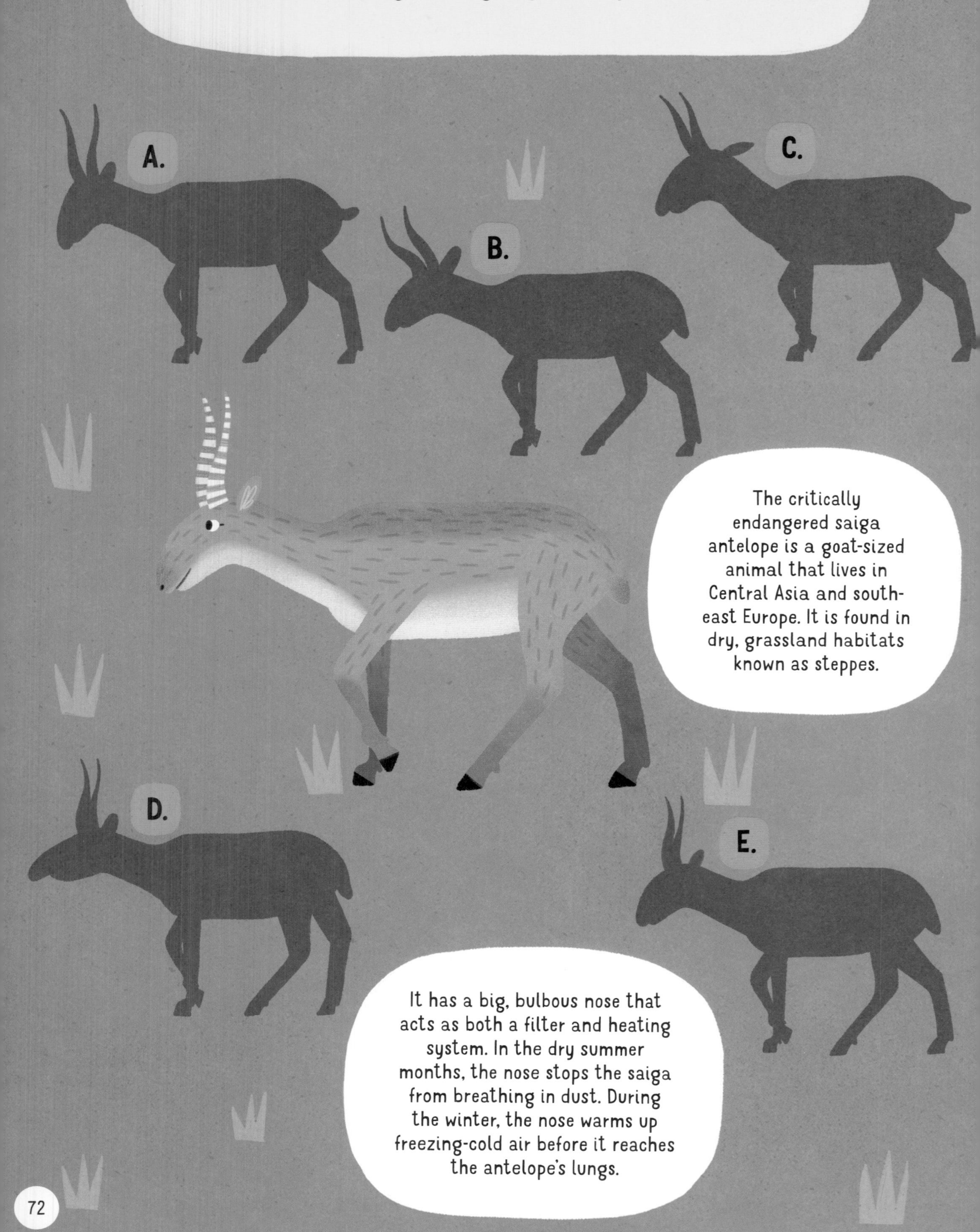

The critically endangered saiga antelope is a goat-sized animal that lives in Central Asia and south-east Europe. It is found in dry, grassland habitats known as steppes.

It has a big, bulbous nose that acts as both a filter and heating system. In the dry summer months, the nose stops the saiga from breathing in dust. During the winter, the nose warms up freezing-cold air before it reaches the antelope's lungs.

PRZEWALSKI PICTURE PUZZLE

Which of the tiles below are not from this picture of a herd of Przewalkski horses?

Przewalkski (pronounced 'shuh-VAL-skee') horses are the last truly wild species of horse left in the world. They are named after a Russian explorer who discovered them in the 1870s.

By the 1960s, Przewalkski horses had become extinct in the wild. Thanks to conservation efforts, herds have now been successfully reintroduced to areas of Mongolia and China.

SILVERBACK STRENGTH

Can you complete the number pyramids below? Each square contains a number that is equal to the sum of the two beneath it. The mountain gorilla with the largest total at the top is the strongest – which one is it?

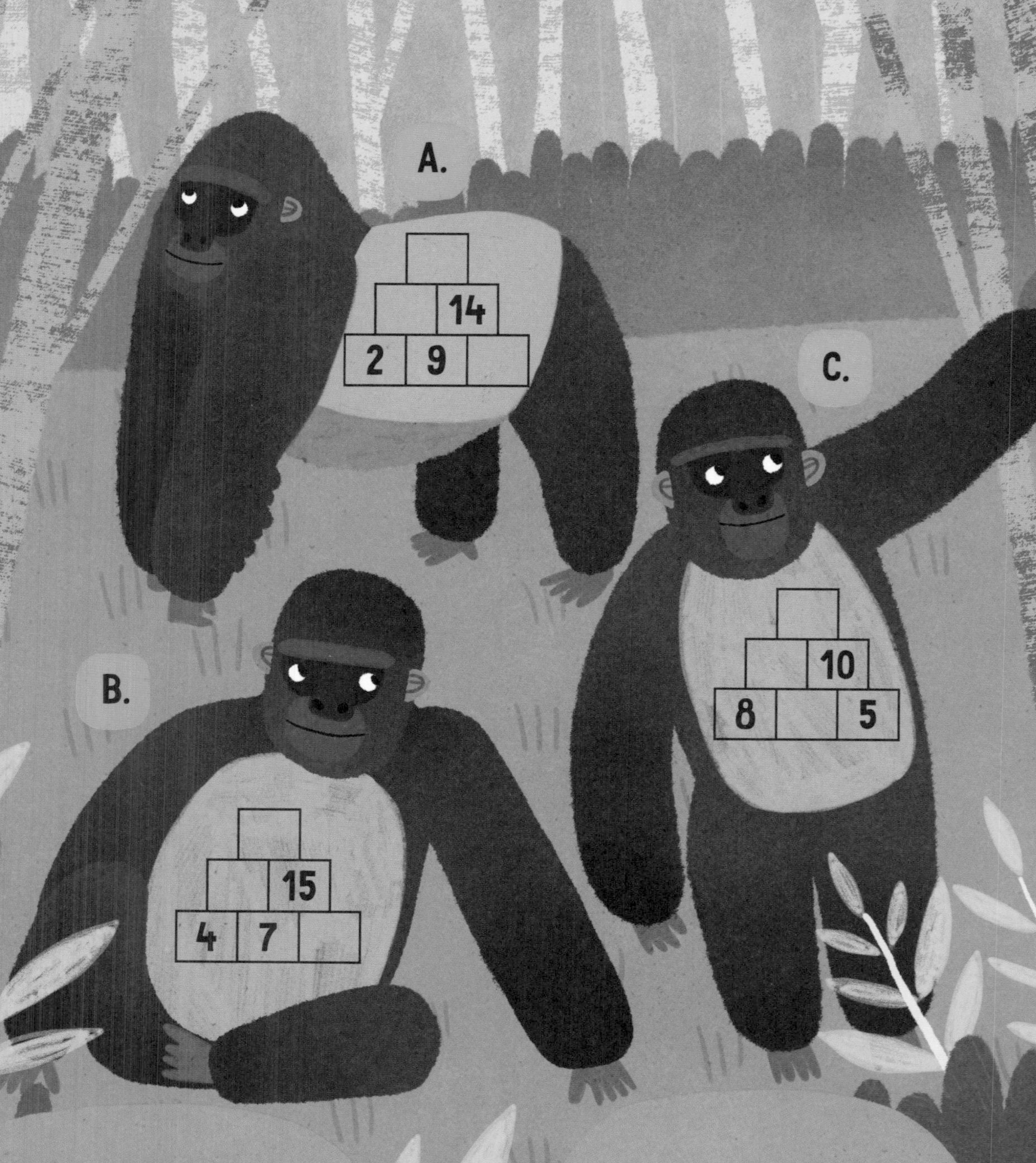

Only around 1,000 mountain gorillas are thought to be left in the world. As their name suggests, these gorillas live in lush, mountain forests in Uganda, Rwanda and the Democratic Republic of Congo.

Mountain gorillas have thicker fur than other great apes. They live at altitudes of 1,500–4,000 m where temperatures can drop below freezing, so it's important they keep warm.

OKAPI TRAIL

Can you work out this okapi's favourite trail through the rainforest? Use the clues and key to find out what to do at each landmark you encounter. Where is the okapi's final destination?

When you reach a rock, turn north.
When you reach a buttress root, turn east.
When you reach a fern, turn south.
When you reach a water pool, turn west.

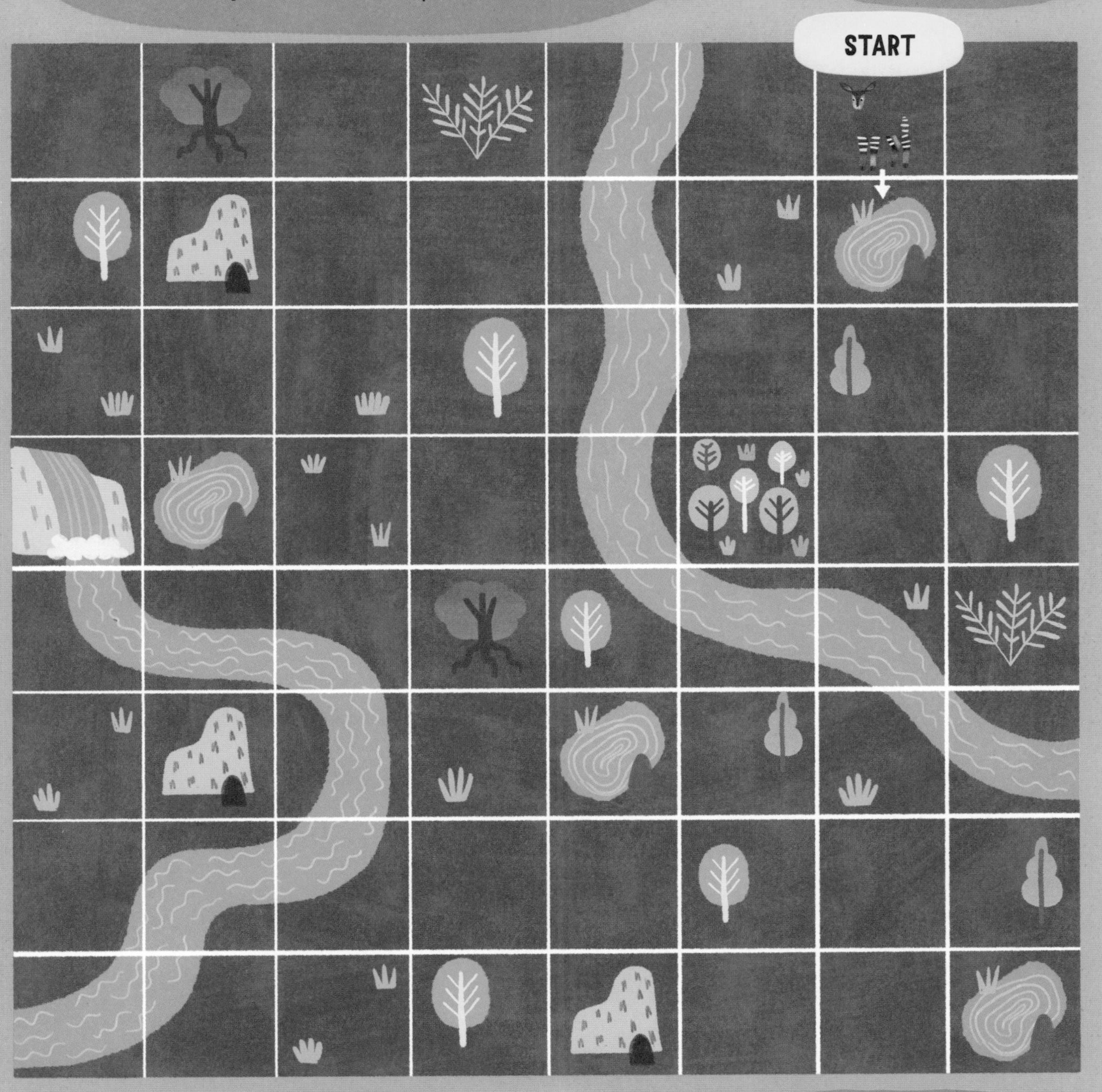

Although okapis look a bit like zebras, they are actually related to giraffes. The striped pattern on an okapi's legs helps it camouflage in the jungle by breaking up its silhouette.

Okapis have smelly feet! As an okapi patrols its territory, scent glands on the bottom of its feet leave behind a sticky substance, which lets other okapis know that bit of forest is taken.

KAKAPO GO!

Help this kakapo through the forest to its burrow, completing each challenge that you land on. You can play this game by yourself or with other players – you just need a counter for each player and a dice.

START

Count the numbe of kiwi birds in th forest. Move forwa this number of places.

You've found a short cut! Take the path over the log.

Count the number of flowers and the number of moths. Add them together and move forward this number of spaces.

Kakapos are said to smell really nice. They have a sweet, earthy odour, which is thought to help the birds find one another in the thick forests.

You've found some tasty fern roots to eat and feel re-energized. Move forward 2 spaces.

Kakapos live in the mossy, ferny rimu forests (rimu is a type of evergreen tree) of New Zealand. They are the heaviest parrots in the world, the only nocturnal parrots and the only parrots that can't fly.

Count the number of yellowhead birds in the forest. Go back this number of spaces.

You've found some tasty fruit and decide to stay here a while. Miss a go.

You think you hear a predator in the bushes and freeze on the spot. Miss a go.

You think you can smell another kakapo. Move back one space to find it.

ount all the other kakapos you can see in the forest before your next go.

Kakapos spend most of their time waddling along the forest floor searching for leaves, flowers and seeds to eat. If they feel threatened, they will freeze on the spot and hope the danger goes away. Only around 150 birds remain in the wild and they live on specially protected islands.

FINISH

SEAL MEAL

Follow the lines to work out what each seal likes to eat.

ANTARCTICA MEMORY GAME

Study this Antarctic scene closely, then turn the page and see how much you can remember.

Antarctica is the coldest, driest and windiest continent on Earth. In spite of these extreme conditions, it's home to 15 species of whale and dolphin, five species of penguin and six species of seal. Every spring, more than 100 million birds breed here.

Arctic terns have the longest migration of any bird. They fly continuously between the Arctic summer and the Antarctic summer, a round trip of about 35,000 km.

ANTARCTICA MEMORY GAME

Study the picture on the previous page and then see how many questions you can answer.

1. How many adult penguins are there?

....

2. How many baby penguins are there?

....

3. Is the seal lying down asleep or awake?

....

4. How many different species of penguin are there in the picture?

....

5. How many birds are flying?

....

6. How many birds have something in their beak, and what is it?

....

ODD ORCA OUT

Can you spot the orca that has a different pattern to the rest?

Orcas will hunt together in groups called pods. They have even been known to swim right up to a beach in order to catch sea lions before wriggling back into the water.

Although they are also known as 'killer whales', orcas actually belong to the dolphin family.

FIT FOR A FOX

Can you work out which garden this fox's den is in?

CLUES:

1. There is a shed in the garden.
2. There isn't a bird table.
3. The garden has a pond in it.
4. The garden has more than 10 flowers in it but fewer than 15.

Red foxes are extremely adaptable and are as at home in towns as they are in the countryside. In 2011, during the construction of the Shard, the UK's tallest skyscraper, a fox was found living on the 72nd floor!

One of an urban fox's favourite places to live is under a garden shed. Foxes are inquisitive creatures and will play with objects lying around a garden, such as gardening gloves or dog toys.

SUDOKU SUPPER

Complete this sudoku puzzle, so that every row, column and 2x3 mini-grid contains all six of this hedgehog's favourite things to eat. Use the smaller example grid to see how it works.

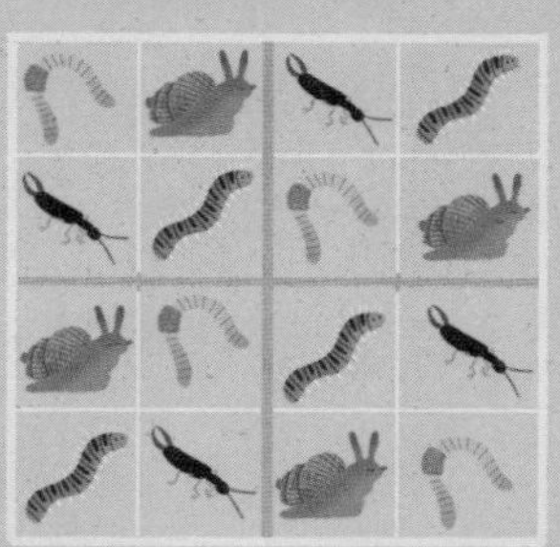

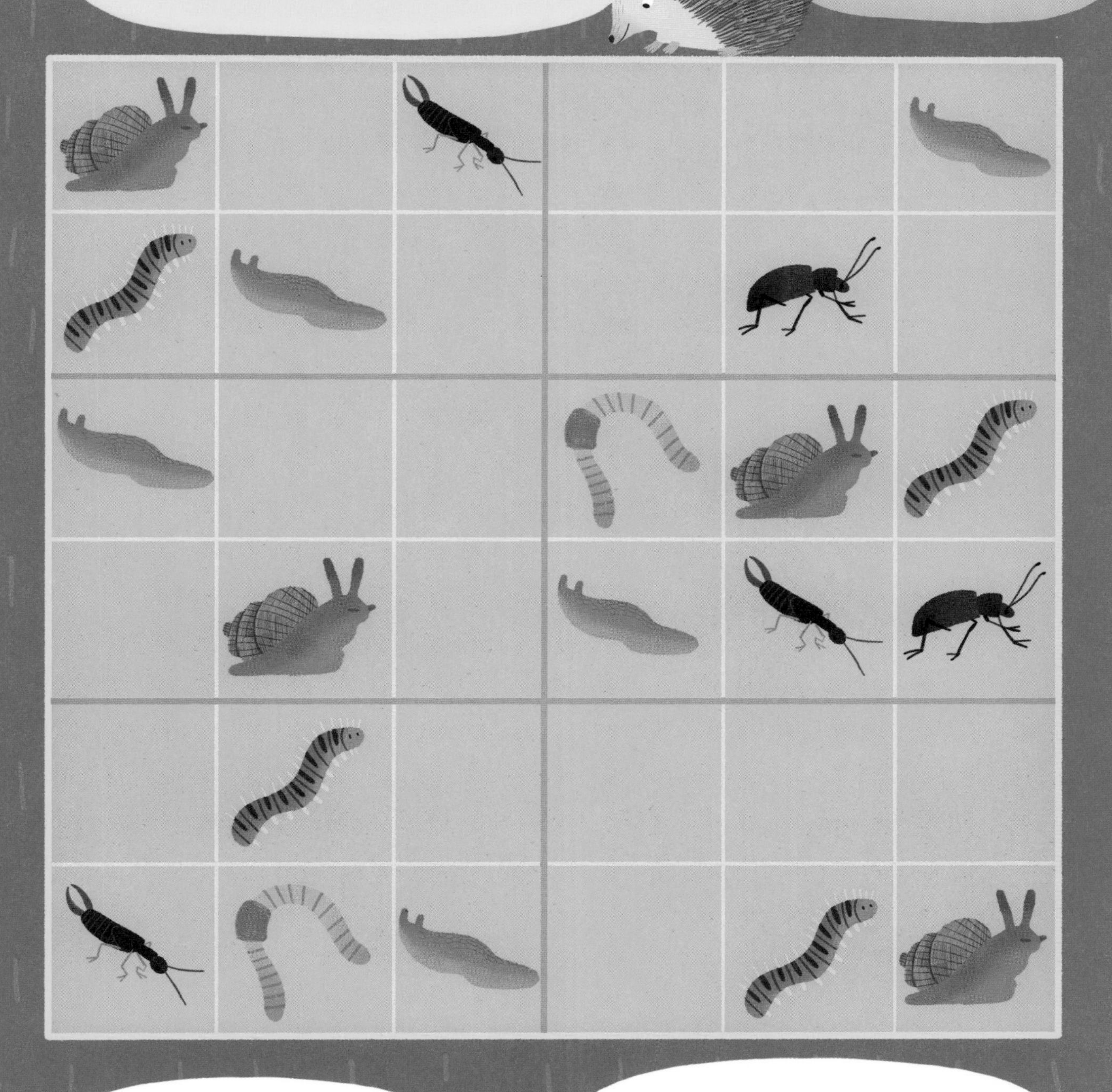

When a hedgehog is born, the spines that cover its body are soft and short. They harden as the hedgehog grows up. An adult hedgehog has between 5,000 and 7,000 spines, all around 2-3 cm long.

The number of hedgehogs in the UK has fallen massively in the last 50 years - from 30 million in the 1950s to 1 million in 2018. Wherever you live, letting areas of grass grow wild in your garden and making holes in the fence so hedgehogs can move between gardens are a few ways to help them out.

WHICH AFRICAN CAT ARE YOU?

Answer the following questions to find out your African cat match.

1. Which is your favourite place to be?
   A. In a large group **B.** Up a tree **C.** In a small group **D.** On your own
2. What is your favourite pastime?
   A. Sleeping **B.** Climbing **C.** Sprinting **D.** High jump
3. What is your favourite habitat?
   A. Grasslands **B.** You're happy just about anywhere
   C. Open plains or desert **D.** Wetlands
4. What is your favourite time of day?
   A. Evening **B.** Night time **C.** Morning **D.** Any time of day
5. Which of the following most accurately describes you?
   A. Loud **B.** Adaptable **C.** Athletic **D.** A good listener

If you answered mainly As ... you're a lion.

Lions live in large family groups. They are the loudest big cat. A male lion's roar can be heard for up to 8 km.

If you answered mainly Bs ... you're a leopard.

Leopards are very adaptable and live in lots of different habitats, from open grasslands to dense jungle. They are also excellent climbers.

If you answered mainly Cs ... you're a cheetah.

These quick-footed cats are the fastest land animals in the world and can reach speeds of 112 km per hour.

If you answered mainly Ds ... you're a serval.

These unique-looking felines have the largest ears of any cat. They can jump nearly 3 m to catch birds from the air.

GIRAFFE PATTERN

Can you find a trail from the the top of this reticulated giraffe's head to the tip of its foot by only passing through touching patches that have six sides? The patches where you should start and finish have been highlighted for you.

Reticulated giraffes are found in Kenya, Somalia and Ethiopia. They have particularly distinctive patterns on their fur, formed of large patches separated by pale lines. The pattern on a giraffe's coat is unique to that animal, much like a human's fingerprints.

Giraffes are the tallest animals in the world. Males can be 5.5 m tall and their legs alone are taller than most humans! Their height allows them to keep a look out for predators as well as reach the tender buds at the very top of their favourite acacia trees.

COUNT THE CAPYBARAS

How many capybaras can you count in this wetland scene?

These semi-aquatic mammals are found in lakes, ponds and rivers throughout South America. They are the largest rodents in the world.

Female capybaras give birth to four or five young. To keep the babies safe, groups of mothers will come together to raise their young in large groups – a bit like a giant, rodent nursery.

TANGLED TONGUES

Can you work out which hummingbird is feeding from which flower?

A hummingbird can visit up to 1,000 flowers – and drink up to 10,000 calories of nectar – in just one day.

A hummingbird's tongue is so long that, when it's not being used, it curls around the bird's eyes inside its skull. There are tiny hairs on the tip of its tongue that helps the bird to lap up nectar from flowers.

ODD FISH OUT

This green sea turtle is getting its shell cleaned by a group of tropical fish. All of the fish have an identical twin apart from one. Can you spot the odd fish out?

Tang fish gather together in large groups to form 'cleaning stations' on tropical reefs. Green sea turtles swim to these stations and allow the tang (and other fish) to eat algae and parasites off their shell and skin.

Cleaning the turtle helps the fish because they get a meal. Having a clean shell also allows the turtle to move smoothly through the water and removing parasites helps it stay healthy. This sort of process – when different species work together in a way that benefits the other – is called 'symbiosis'.

CUBAN CRAB GRID

Can you find these groups of crabs in this giant swarm?

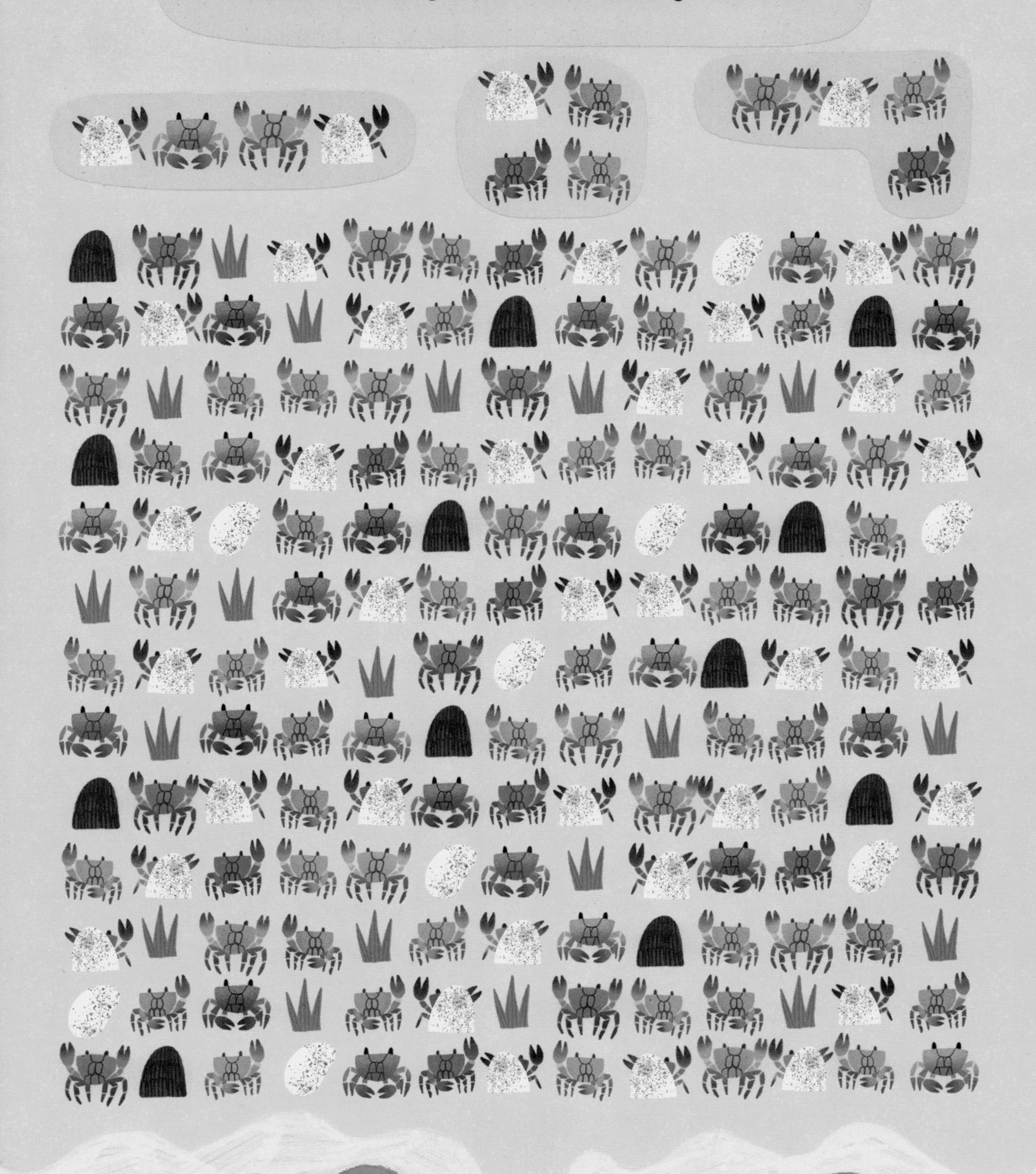

Every spring, millions of black, red and yellow crabs leave their homes in Cuba's forests and scuttle down to the sea to lay their eggs. Once the eggs hatch, the baby crabs make their way back to the forest a few weeks later.

Although these crabs are land crabs and cannot survive in the sea for long, they still need to keep their gills moist in order to breathe. They dig deep burrows in the forest to keep themselves damp.

WHOSE EGG IS WHOSE?

Follow the lines to find out which egg belongs to each of these Australian animals.

The duck-billed platypus and four species of echidna are very unusual mammals because they lay eggs (rather than give birth to their young). These egg-laying mammals are known as 'monotremes' and they are only found in Australia and New Guinea.

Emus and cassowaries are Australia's largest birds. The males of both species are responsible for incubating their eggs and raising the chicks.

WHO FLEDGED FIRST?

These budgerigar chicks have just left the nest or 'fledged'. Can you use the following clues to work out the order in which they fledged?

1. Chick A left the nest before Chick B but just after Chick D.
2. Chick C left the nest after Chick B but before Chick E.

Wild budgerigars are small green-and-yellow parakeets that are found in large flocks throughout Australia. Flocks are normally made up of around 100 birds but during rainy seasons they can number several thousands.

The name 'budgerigar' is believed to come from a word in the Gamilaraay language, 'betcherrygah', which means 'good food'. It's thought that Indigenous Australians followed flocks of migrating budgies to places of food.

BAMBOO BRAIN-TEASER

Giant pandas need to eat around 38 kg of bamboo a day. Can you guide this panda through the bamboo forest so it eats up exactly 38 kg of bamboo?

Each square contains an equation that will give the total amount of bamboo the panda can eat in that area. You must land on just three separate squares to reach your total of 38 kg. Write down the co-ordinates of the squares at the bottom of the page when you're finished.

	A	B	C	D
6				
5			6 kg x 7 kg	8 kg x 10 kg
4	12 kg x 4 kg	3 kg x 3 kg	2 kg x 5 kg	3 kg x 10 kg
3	10 kg x 10 kg	4 kg x 9 kg	7 kg x 5 kg	3 kg x 8 kg
2	1 kg x 30 kg	4 kg x 4 kg	9 kg x 9 kg	8 kg x 8kg
1	5 kg x 9 kg	2 kg x 12 kg	10 kg x 8 kg	3 kg x 12 kg

6 kg x 10 kg
10 kg x 10 kg
Giant pandas live in remote bamboo forests in the mountains of central China. Although these bears are omnivores and will eat fish and small animals, bamboo makes up a whopping 99 per cent of their diet.
4 kg x 6 kg
9 kg x 6 kg
7 kg x 8 kg
8 kg x 3 kg
11 kg x 5 kg
5 kg x 5 kg
3 kg x 4 kg
5 kg x 6 kg
2 kg x 9 kg
4 kg x 7 kg
4 kg x 10 kg
Giant pandas are vulnerable animals – it is thought that only around 1,800 remain in the wild. Females usually give birth to one or two cubs. The babies are pink when they're born and measure about 15 cm – that's about the size of a pencil! They are born blind and only open their eyes when they are about eight weeks old.
5 kg x 3 kg
ANSWER:
E
F
G
H

SEA OTTER SEARCH

To stop themselves from floating away while feeding or sleeping, sea otters will wrap themselves in a seaweed called kelp. Can you spot a sea otter among the rocks and kelp below?

Sea otters are found in kelp forests along the Pacific coasts of North America. The kelp provides a habitat for sea urchins – the otters' favourite food. When feeding, an otter will lie on its back, place a rock on its stomach and hammer the urchin against it to break open the shell.

Unlike other marine mammals, sea otters don't have a layer of blubber (or fat) to keep them warm. Instead, they have incredibly thick fur – in fact, a sea otter's coat is denser than any other animal's. An adult male's coat may contain up to 800 million hair fibres.

SWAMP SUM
Each of these three mother alligators has 15 baby alligators. How many babies are missing from the picture below?
American alligators are found in rivers, lakes and swamps in Louisiana and Florida. The species is thought to be 150 million years old, meaning that alligators were around when dinosaurs roamed the Earth.
Female alligators build nests of leaves and mud, and lay between 20 and 60 eggs. Baby alligators are about 15 cm long when they hatch and are protected by their mother for the first few years of their lives. Alligators are one of the few reptile species that care for their young.

LEAPING LEMURS

A sifaka lemur can jump up to 9 m in a single leap. Can you take this sifaka to its friend on the other side of the clearing by only leaping on touching patches of earth that contain a total of 9?

Sifakas are unusual because they don't get around in the way that other lemurs do. They have very long, powerful back legs that allow them to spring through the trees while remaining upright. They also stay on two feet when on the ground.

Sifaka lemurs – like all lemurs – are native to the island of Madagascar, off the south-east coast of Africa.

CHAMELEON PAIRS

All of these chameleons have an identical twin – apart from one. Can you spot it?

There are around 150 species of chameleon in the world and nearly half of them are found on the island of Madagascar.

Special cells in a chameleon's skin allow it to change colour. This isn't just to help the animal blend in with its surroundings – a chameleon will also change colour to communicate with other chameleons or to attract a mate.

SNAKE SUMS

Did you know that female Burmese pythons 'hug' their eggs? They vibrate their muscles as they squeeze the eggs to keep their body temperature high and their eggs warm. Solve the calculation chains below to find out some more super facts about these snakes. Start with the number on the left and perform each sum in turn to get the final result.

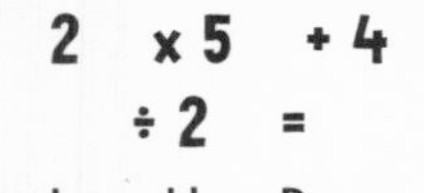

2 × 5 + 4 ÷ 2 =

the length a Burmese python can grow to in metres.

100 - 4 ÷ 4 + 1 =

the average lifespan of these snakes in the wild.

15 + 6 × 4 + 16 =

the number of eggs a female can lay in a clutch.

25 × 2 + 40 ÷ 3 =

the number of minutes they can stay underwater for. Burmese pythons are excellent swimmers.

DRAGON ISLAND

Komodo dragons are found on Indonesia's Lesser Sunda Islands. Study the map below, then use the compass to answer the following questions about this unique habitat.

1. What natural landmark is in the island's southwestern corner? ....
2. What is immediately east of the palm trees? ....
3. How many Timor deer are in the northeastern corner of the island? ....
4. Is the watering hole in the north or west of the island, and how many water buffalo are visiting it? ....
5. How many Komodo dragons are there on the island altogether? ....

BACK WITH THE PACK

Can you reunite this lone wolf with the rest of its pack by finding a trail through the forest? To reach the pack, you must follow the trees in the order shown below. You can move across, up and down through the forest but not diagonally.

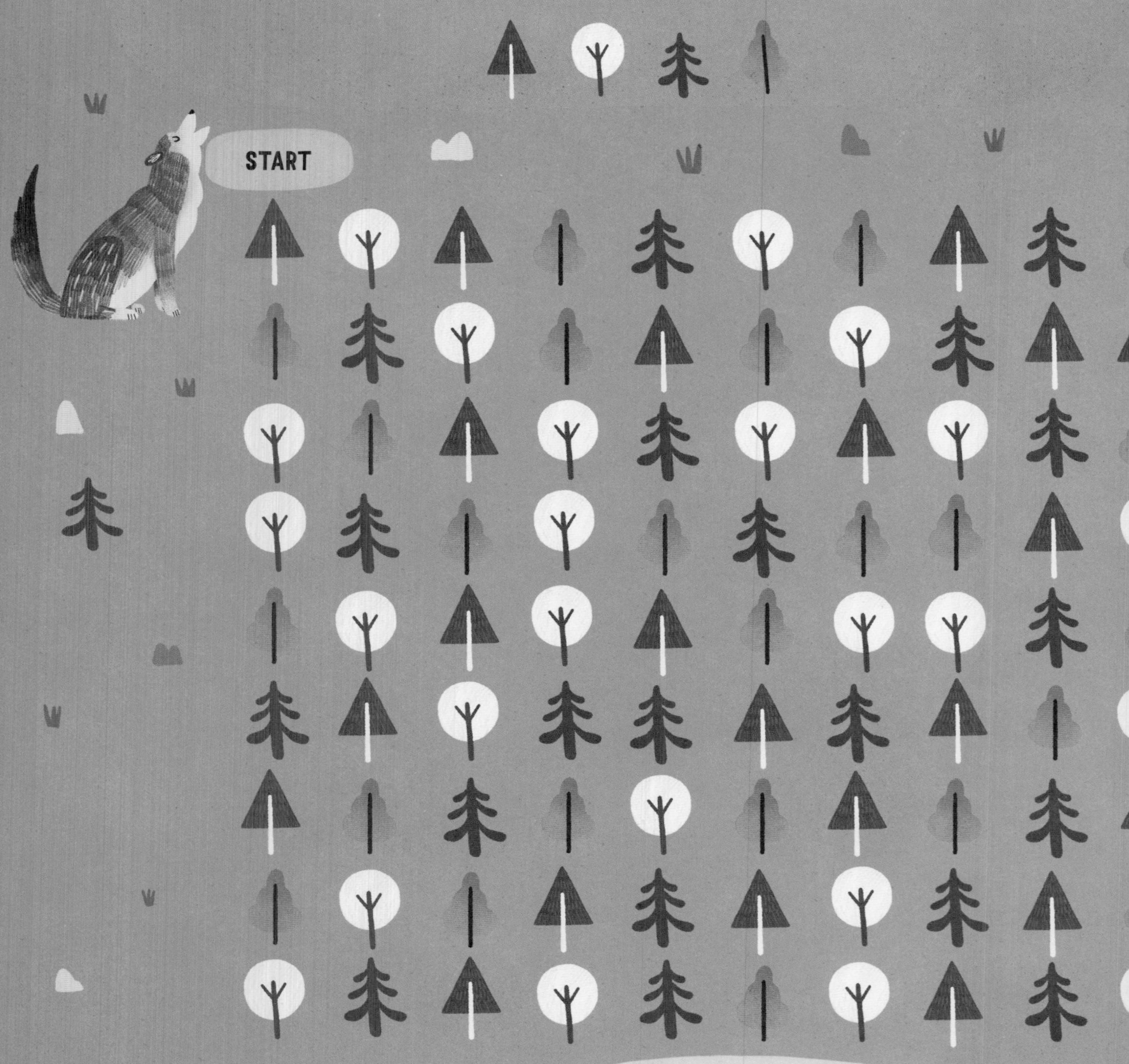

Wolves don't howl at the moon, but they do howl to communicate with one another and claim territory. A wolf's howl can be heard up to 10 km in a forest. They will also howl as a group together – this is thought to strengthen bonds.

Grey wolves live in packs of around ten animals, which are usually lead by an alpha (or head) male and female and their pups from several seasons. The alpha couple mate for life and are normally the only pair in the pack that produce puppies. However, other wolves in the pack will also help care for and raise their younger siblings.

FINISH

Wolves work as a team to hunt. They can roam large distances – up to 20 km a day – in their search for food. When they have a successful hunt they don't hold back. An adult will eat around 9 kg in one sitting. That's the equivalent of you having 26 beef burgers for lunch!

SWALLOW MIGRATION

Can you guide this swallow back to its home? Use the clues and key to find out what to do at each landmark you encounter. Where is the swallow's final destination?

When you reach a forest, fly north.
When you reach a town, fly south.

When you reach a lake, fly east.
When you reach a mountain, fly west.

There are 90 species of swallow around the world. Several species in Europe and North America undertake extremely long migrations every year, often returning each time to the place they were raised.

A common swallow in the UK, for example, will travel to South Africa and back twice a year to breed and find food – a distance of around 10,000 km. These tiny birds fly approximately 300 km a day, at about 30 km per hour.

A BUG'S LIFE

The pictures below represent the unusual life cycles of three different insects – a peacock butterfly, a ladybird and a stag beetle. Can you work out which life cycle is which, and put them in the correct order? Look closely at the habitats in each picture to help you.

If a peacock butterfly feels threatened, it can create a hissing sound by rubbing its wings together. This, along with the eyespots on its wings, will scare off predators such as mice and birds. The noise is loud enough to be heard by humans.

The larval (grub) stage of a stag beetle can last for six years. The grubs feed on dead wood, but the adult beetles don't really eat at all. The large jaws that male stag beetles have are used for fighting rather than eating.

PUFFIN MAZE

Guide these three puffin parents to their chicks. By adding up the number of fish in each parent's beak with the number of bonus fish they pick up inside their tunnel, can you work out which chick will get the most fish?

Atlantic puffins spend most of their lives at sea but gather in large colonies on land each spring to breed. Puffins nest in burrows – either old rabbit burrows or tunnels that they have dug out themselves. A puffin pair will have a single chick (a 'puffling'), which they will raise together.

A puffin's beak is grey for most of the year but turns orange in spring to help the bird attract a mate. Atlantic puffins can carry around ten fish in their beaks at once. A puffin in the UK was once recorded carrying a whopping 62 fish in its beak.

HARVEST MICE PICTURE PUZZLE

Can you find the following pieces in the picture of these tiny harvest mice? Write your co-ordinates underneath each piece.

Harvest mice are the smallest rodents in Europe – their average weight is 4–6 g. They are the only mammals in the UK to have a 'prehensile' tail. This means that the mouse can use its tail to grab hold of things, a bit like an arm.

Harvest mice build round, woven grass nests high up off the ground – usually between stalks of corn or long grass.

BUTTERFLY LINES

Can you divide up this butterfly scene into four sections using just three lines? Each section should contain one of each type of butterfly.

'Mud-puddling' butterflies are a common sight in the Amazon rainforest. The butterflies look like they are sitting in a muddy puddle, but they are actually sucking up salt and nutrients found in the wet soil. Butterflies will also drink nutrients from animal dung, tears, sweat and even blood.

The largest butterfly found in the Amazon rainforest is the blue morpho butterfly. Its giant, electric-blue wings span between 12 and 20 cm.

DOT-TO-DOT SPOTS

Join the dots to complete the picture of a rare rainforest cat. Don't let its spots confuse you!

HIPPO STATS

Solve these calculation chains to reveal some big stats about these river giants. Start with the number on the left and perform each sum in turn to get the final result.

75 + 25 x 11 + 200 =
the average weight of an adult female hippo in kilograms. Males can weigh over twice as much.

100 ÷ 2 - 25 ÷ 5 =
how long a hippo can hold its breath underwater in minutes. A hippo can close its ears and nostrils when it dives, to keep water out.

2 x 6 + 6 - 3 + 20 =
the amount of grass a hippo can eat in one night in kilograms. Hippos only leave the water and come on land to eat when it gets dark.

5 x 6 ÷ 2 + 5 =
the number of hippos in a typical herd. Groups are led by a dominant male.

AARDVARK CO-ORDINATES

Can you use the co-ordinates to answer the following questions about this aardvark's night-time walk? Start at the aardvark's burrow at A,9.

1. Where does he stop at C,9? ....
2. What does he reach at D,8? ....
3. Where does he head to at F,5? ....
4. What does he find at D,2? ....
5. Where does he end up at G,3? ....

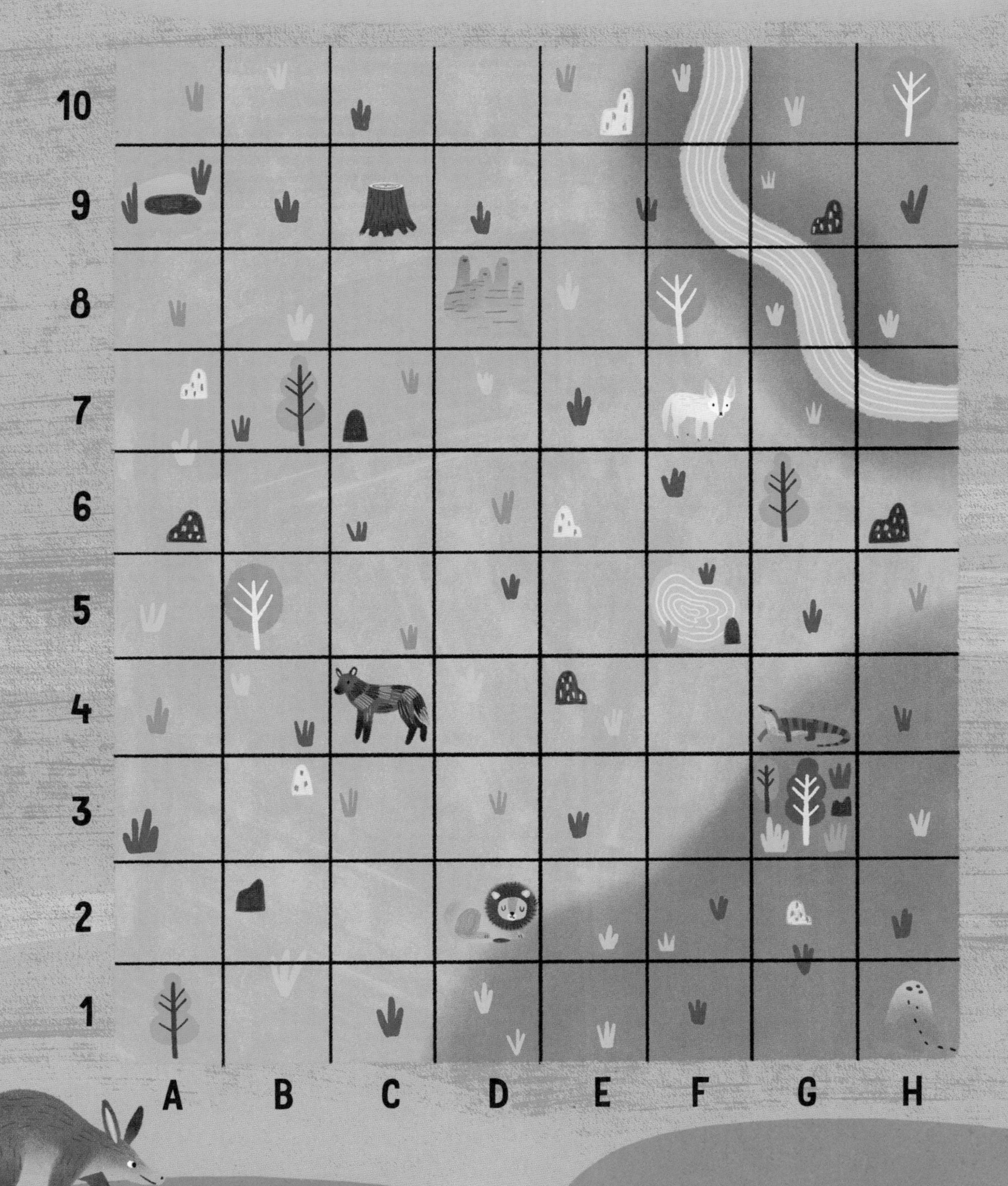

The name 'aardvark' means 'earth pig' in South Africa's Afrikaans language. Aardvarks travel several kilometres a night in search of their favourite food – termites.

An aardvark will break into termite mounds with its large claws and is able to close its nostrils to stop angry termites from crawling up its snout.

RACCOON RAID

These security cameras have caught some pictures of raccoons foraging in this neighbourhood's bins. Can you work out which camera took which picture? Draw straight lines from the cameras to help you.

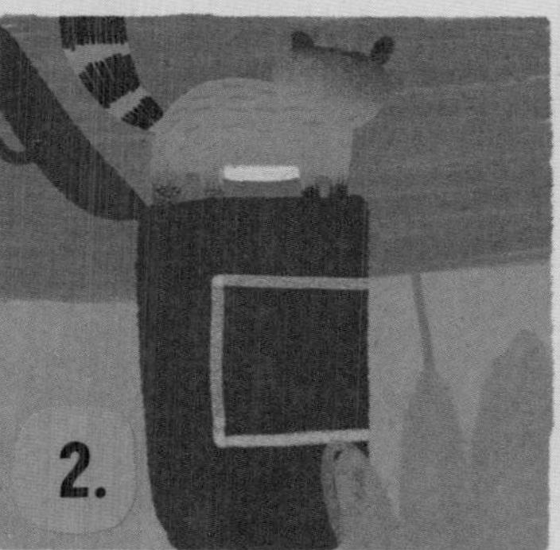

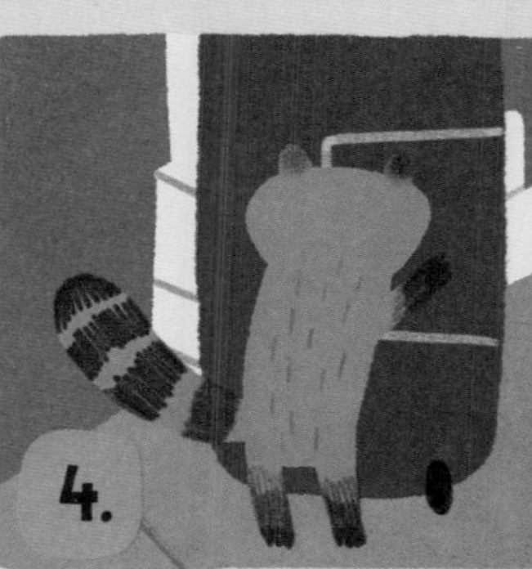

Raccoons are incredibly adaptable creatures and are found in all sorts of habitats throughout North America – from forests and marshes to cities. They'll eat fruit, nuts, fish, meat and whatever they can find in humans' rubbish bins.

Their long, dexterous hands are very sensitive. Raccoons have four to five more sensory cells in their paws than most other mammals. This means that they can 'see' an object just by touching it (without actually looking at it).

BALD EAGLE REFLECTIONS

Which of these reflections belongs to this bald eagle?

Although bald eagles will feed on small mammals, fish is their main food source and they are often found around lakes, rivers and on the coast. They can dive at speeds of up to 160 km an hour to snatch a fish from the water.

The bald eagle is the national bird of the United States and the only eagle unique to North America.

MANGROVE SWAMP SEARCH AND FIND

How many of the following rare creatures can you find in this mangrove swamp?

KEY

BENGAL TIGER

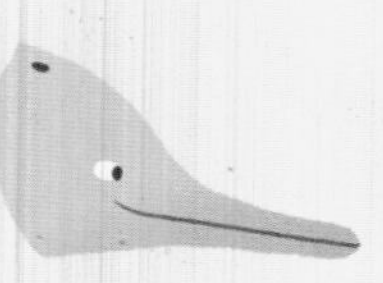
GANGES RIVER DOLPHIN

MUDSKIPPER

BROWN-WINGED KINGFISHER

HORSESHOE CRAB

NORTHERN RIVER TERRAPIN

Mudskipper fish live in marshes and estuaries. They are able to emerge from the water and 'skip' about on land.

Mangrove horseshoe crabs are often called 'living fossils' because their size and shape has remained unchanged for millions of years.
The Ganges river dolphin is a rare species of freshwater dolphin. It has very weak eyes and is essentially blind. It hunts by making ultrasonic sounds that bounce off the fish and allow the dolphin to locate its prey.

WHERE'S THE WOODPECKER?

Can you find all of the woodpeckers in this desert? The numbers around the edge of the grid tell you how many woodpeckers appear in each row and column. A woodpecker can only be found horizontally or vertically next to a cactus, and woodpeckers are never next to each other, neither vertically, horizontally nor diagonally. Look at the example on the right to see how the puzzle works.

EXAMPLE:

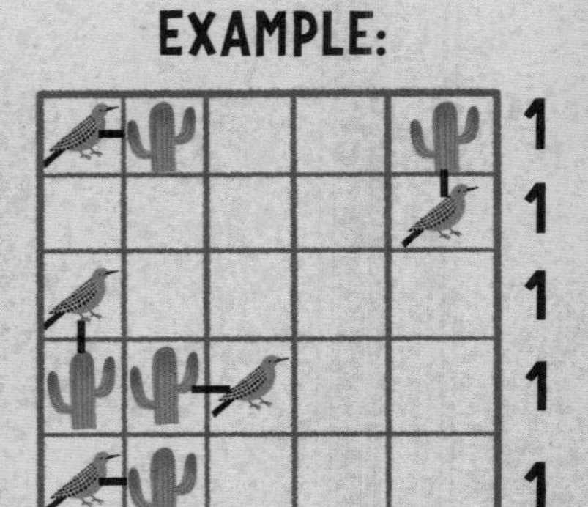

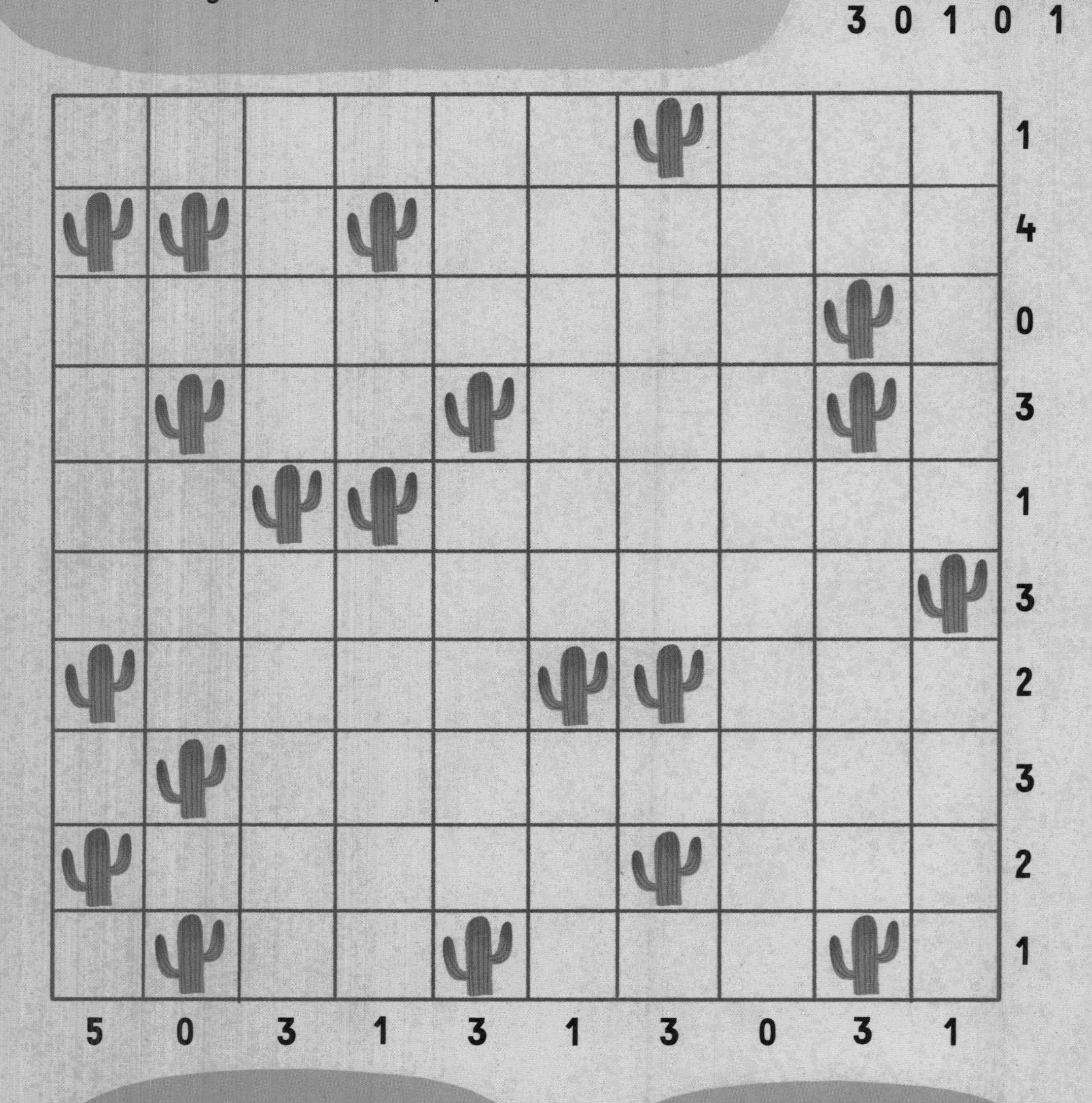

Gila woodpeckers make their nests in giant saguaro cacti found throughout desert regions of the southern United States and Mexico. They carve holes out with their beaks without damaging the plants and feed on the cacti's flowers.

Once a woodpecker's chicks have left the nest, the hole is used by other desert birds, such as owls and flycatchers.

AMERICAN DESERT ANIMALS: TRUE OR FALSE?

Can you sort the true facts from the fibs in this quiz about American desert animals?

ELF OWL

1. Male bighorn sheep use their large, curly horns to fight one another. They can charge at speeds of up to 32 km per hour.
2. Coyotes are picky eaters and only eat deer or bighorn sheep.
3. Bobcats live in large family groups called prides, as lions do.
4. Despite their name, jackrabbits are hares not rabbits.
5. Like most lizards, gila monsters are not venomous.
6. Gila monsters do not eat very often – they can survive on just three big meals a year.
7. There are 29 species of rattlesnake. The snake gets a new rattle each time it sheds its skin.
8. Greater roadrunners can run faster than any other type of bird.
9. Found in the deserts of the southern USA and Mexico, the elf owl is the smallest owl in the world.
10. Desert kit foxes spend most of the day hunting in the desert and rest in cool burrows at night.

GILA MONSTER

JACKRABBIT

DESERT KIT FOX

SAVANNA JIGSAW

Which tiles below are not from this picture of a savanna scene?

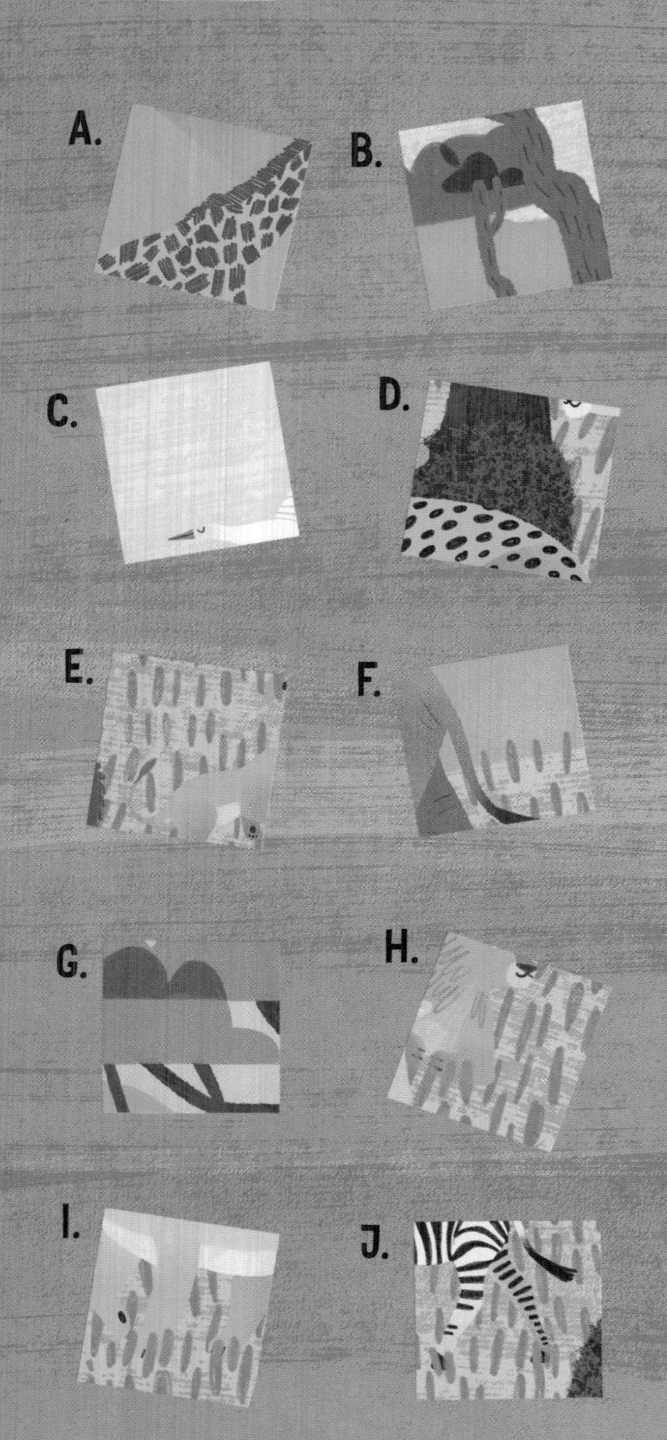

Savannas are tropical grassland habitats. Almost half of Africa is covered in savannas, which provide a home for an incredible range of wildlife, including elephants, giraffes, zebras and lions.

Lions once roamed throughout Africa. Today, they are considered vulnerable and are threatened by habitat loss.

Lions can spend up to 20 hours a day asleep. They tend to hunt in groups at night. Although males always eat first, the females do around 90 per cent of the hunting.

ALL THE ANSWERS

MACAW SEQUENCES P4

TAMARIN TEASER P5

JAVAN RHINO JIGSAW P6

Piece **D**

SUMATRAN TIGER SUMS P7

140 ÷ 2 - 60 x 2 = **20 years**
100 ÷ 2 - 20 ÷ 10 = **3 cubs**
5 + 16 x 10 + 190 = **400**
10 x 20 + 80 ÷ 2 = **140 kg**

TANGLED TWIGS P8

A – Ants
B – Honey
C – Termites

A FLOCK OF FLAMINGOS P9

There are **34** flamingos.

ODD BAT OUT P10

The odd bat out is a brown long-eared bat.

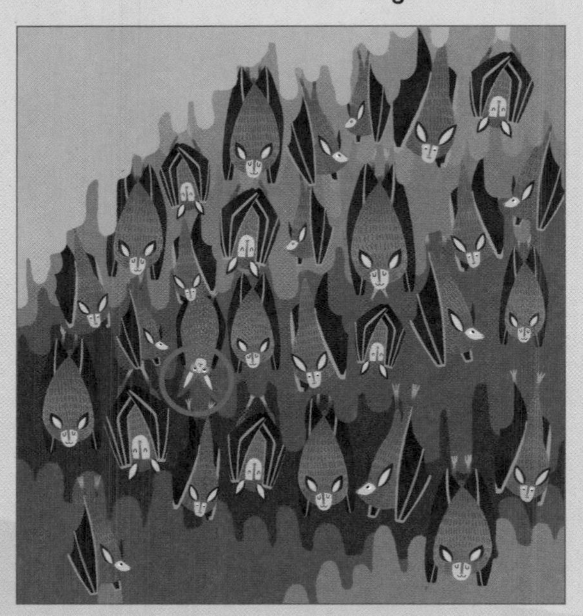

NUTS ABOUT NUTS P11

Squirrel **B**'s store is the **largest** and it's in the **tree**. Squirrel **A**'s store is **medium-sized** and is under the **bush**. Squirrel **C**'s store is the **smallest** and is under the **boulder**.

WHERE'S THE WALLABY? P12

BAFFLED BIRDS P13

A – Bird 2
B – Bird 1
C – Bird 4
D – Bird 3

SALMON MAZE P14–15

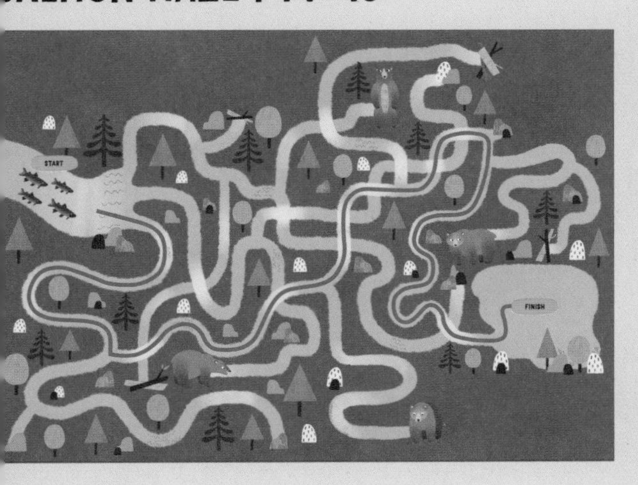

ODD PENGUIN OUT P16–17

SLOTH SILHOUETTE P18

Silhouette **E**

AMAZON RAINFORST QUIZ P19

A. 2 (a jaguar)
B. 1 (hair)
C. 1 (10)
D. 2 (almost 3 km)
E. 2 (the bee hummingbird is the world's smallest bird – there's no such thing as a butterfly hummingbird.)

SNOW LEOPARD SEARCH P20

YAK TRAIL P21

WOODLAND JIGSAW P22

Piece **B**

MARTEN MAZE P23

MIGRATION MAZE P24–25

BLACK BEAR SUMS P26

A. 21 - 7 ÷ 2 x 6 ÷ 2 - 3 = 18 seconds
B. 12 x 5 ÷ 6 x 2 ÷ 10 x 8 = 16 seconds
C. 5 x 3 + 10 x 2 - 14 ÷ 4 = 9 seconds
Bear **C** is the fastest.

COUGAR CO-ORDINATES P27

1. A cave
2. A river
3. A lake
4. A raccoon
5. A tree

ODD SHARK OUT P28

SPOT THE SEA DRAGONS P29

There are **17** leafy sea dragons.

POLAR STEPPING STONES P30

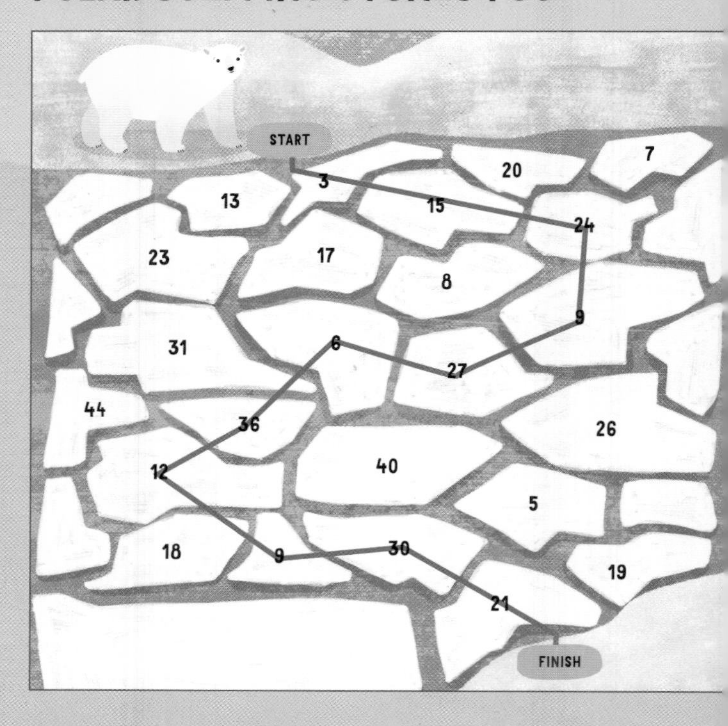

SNOWY OWL SPOT THE DIFFERENCE P31

ANTEATER MAZE P32

ANT TRAIL P33

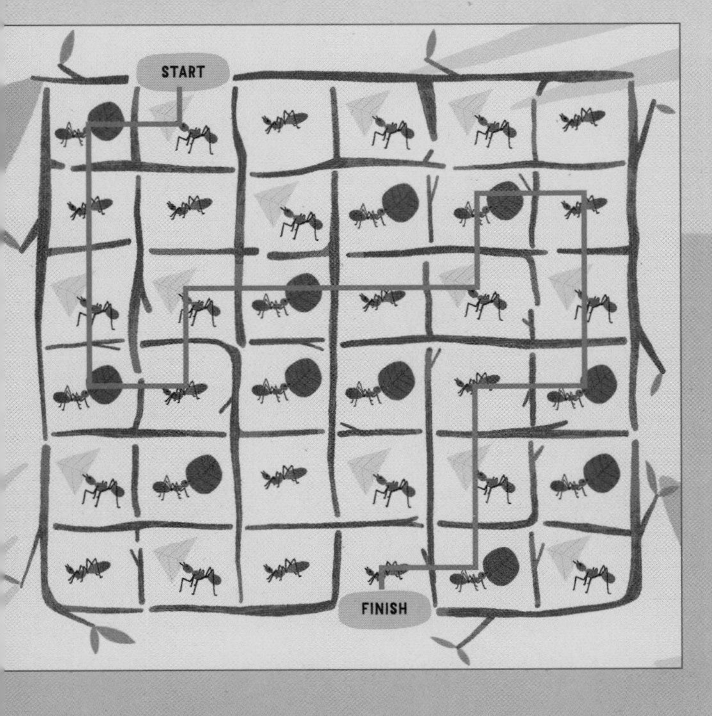

BORNEO SERACH AND FIND P34–35

There is: **1** Bornean orangutan, **1** Borneo pygmy elephant, **1** Sunda clouded leopard, **1** false gharial, **3** Wallace's flying frogs, **2** slow lorises, **1** great hornbill, **2** spiny terrapins, **1** Borneo short-tailed python and **1** proboscis monkey.

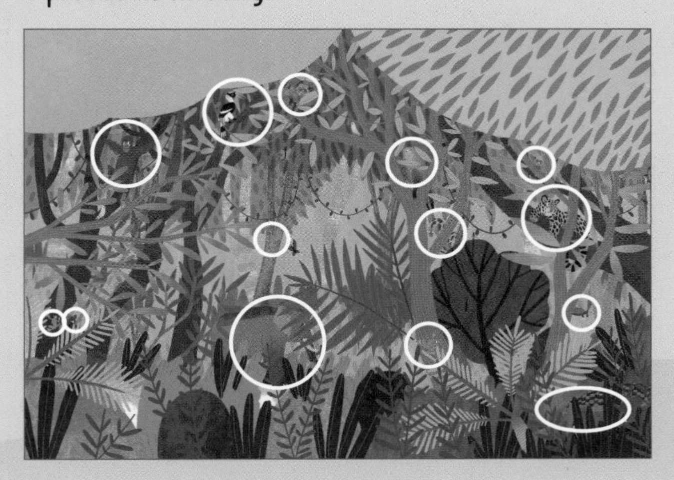

PORCUPINE SILHOUETTE P36

Silhouette **C**

AFRICAN ELEPHANT MEMORY GAME P37–38

1. Five (2 red, 3 pink)
2. Grass or reeds
3. A blue bird
4. Three
5. A dragonfly
6. Two purple birds

MEERKAT SEQUENCES P39

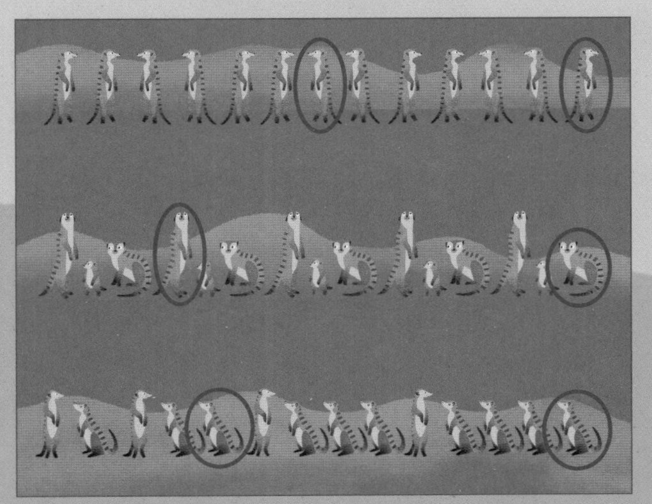

TANGLED TRAILS P40

Trail **C**

BEAVER BRAIN-TEASER P41

The beaver will cut down tree **E**.

AUSTRALIAN ANIMAL MIX-UP P42

Flying fox - C
Bilby - A
Tasmanian devil - F
Koala - E
Wombat - B
Dingo - D

BIRD IN THE BUSH P43

The bird is a **kookaburra**.

MONKEY PUZZLE P44

DANCE PARTNERS P45

A - L
B - J
C - M
D - G
E - K
F - I
H - N

JUNGLE RUN P46–47

The jaguar meets a toucan, the armadillo meets a beetle, the coati meets a frog and the tapir meets a butterfly. The **armadillo** gets to the watering hole.

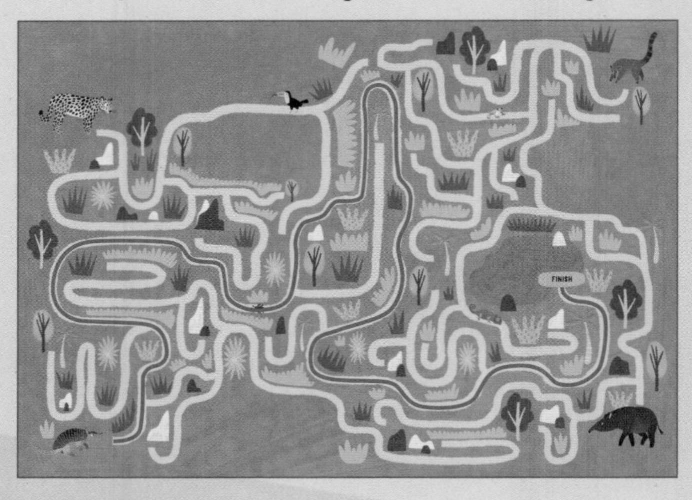

SHY GUY P48

The animal is a **red panda**.

TIGER TERRITORIES P49

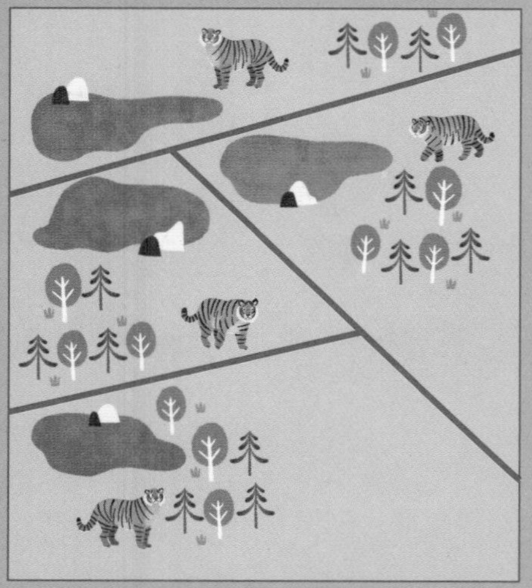

NEST MUDDLE P50–51

- 6 D - 2
- 4 E - 5
- 3 F - 1

POND PUZZLER P52

here are **19** ducklings missing from the picture 4 mallard ducklings and 5 tufted duck ducklings).

BEE BRAIN-TEASER P53

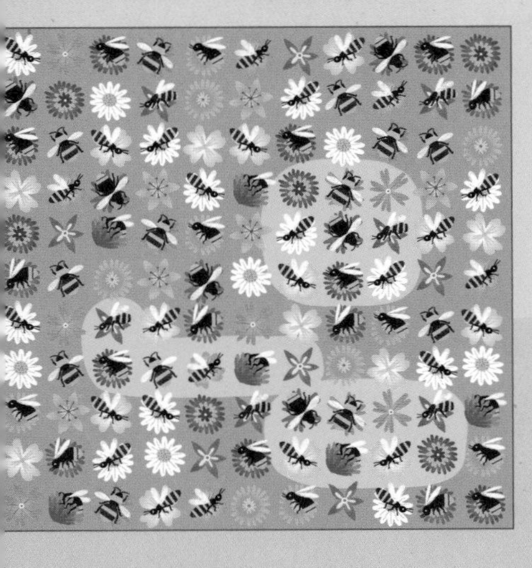

TWIT T-WHO? P54

- Great grey owl D - Long-eared owl
- Great horned owl E - Western screech owl
- Burrowing owl

COUNT THE BISON P55

There are **33** adult bison, **4** calves and **4** moose.

ROCK POOL SPOT THE DIFFERENCE 56–57

INDIAN ANIMALS: TRUE OR FALSE? P58

1. True
2. False - there are only around 2,500 left in the wild.
3. False - they love water.
4. True
5. True
6. False - unlike other bears, sloth bears don't hibernate.
7. True
8. False - the African elephant is larger than the Asian elephant.
9. True
10. True

PEACOCK PUZZLER P59

A. I,9 **D.** C,2
B. B,1 **E.** G,5
C. D,8 **F.** I,2

REINDEER TRAILS P60

A. 4 x 10 ÷ 2 x 20 + 5 = **405 km**
B. 8 x 3 + 5 x 10 - 2 = **288 km**
C. 7 + 4 - 2 x 12 + 15 = **123 km**
D. 5 x 4 + 10 ÷ 3 x 11 = **110 km**
Reindeer **A** travels the furthest.

COUNTING HARES P61

There are **53** Arctic hares in total – **49** white Arctic hares and **4** brown Arctic hares.

BEAR BRUNCH P62

2 honeycombs
2 avocados
2 orchid bulbs
4 hawk moth caterpillars
1 bromeliad heart
2 bunches of palm nuts
1 bunch of acai berries
4 palm weevils

VICUÑA JIGSAW P63

F and **I** are the missing pieces.

BIG LEAPS P64

PERFECT PARTNER P65

Bird **F** is the perfect partner.

MARINE MAZE P66

TORTOISE YEARS P67

Tortoise **D** is the oldest.

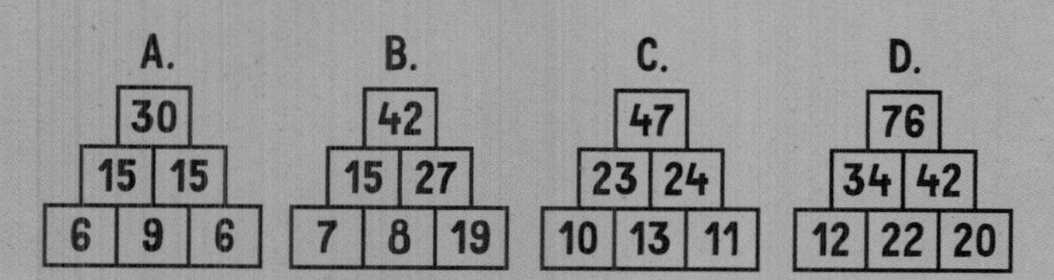

ALBATROSS JOURNEYS P68

The parent who collects green fish collects **65**.
The parent who collects blue fish collects **66**.
So the parent who collects blue fish collects the most.

FOLLOW THE KRILL P69

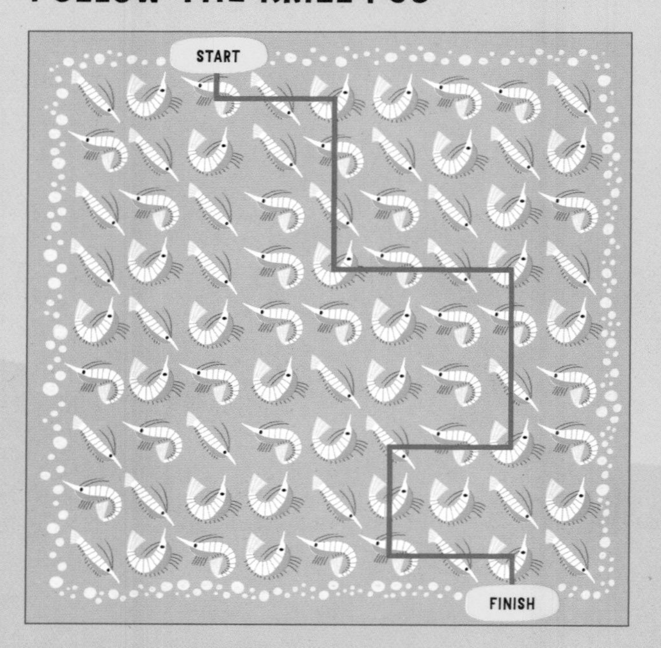

FIND THE FISH P70

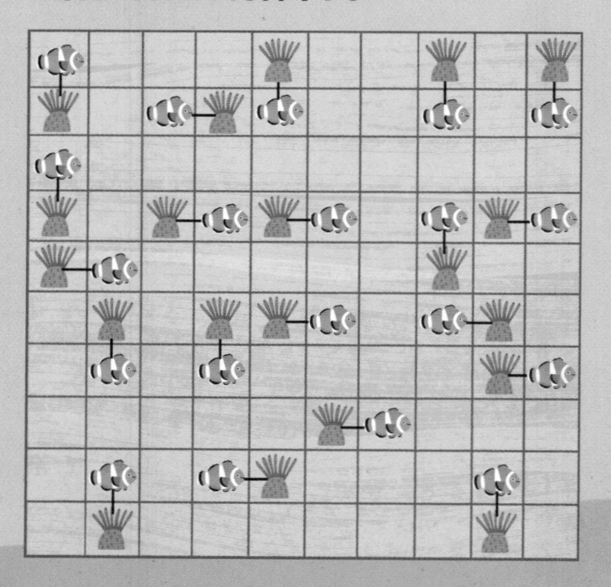

DUGONG DINNER P71

There are 64 seagrass plants in total and the dugong eats 8 plants every 30 minutes. 64 ÷ 8 = 8 lots of 30 mins. There are 2 x 30 mins in 1 hour, so the dungong witll take **4 hours** to eat the whole meadow (8 ÷ 2 = 4).

SAIGA SILHOUETTES P72

Silhouette **E**

PRZEWALSKI PICTURE PUZZLE P73

Tiles **D** and **F** are not in the main picture.

ILVERBACK STRENGTH P74

orilla **B** is the strongest.

A.	B.	C.
25	26	23
11 14	11 15	13 10
2 9 5	4 7 8	8 5 5

KAPI TRAIL P75

he **waterfall** is the okapi's final destination.

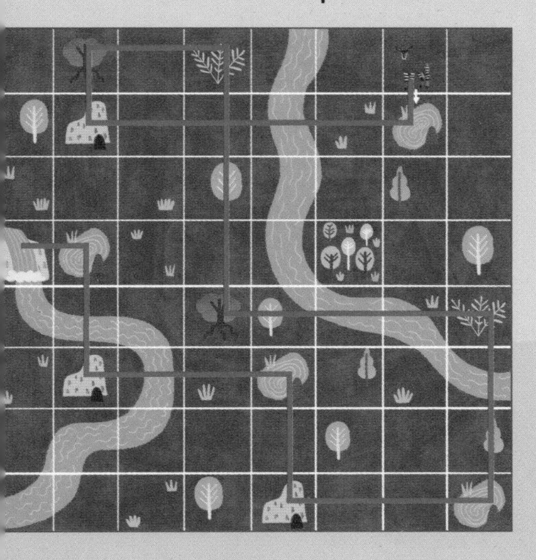

EAL MEAL P78

eopard seal – chinstrap penguin
rabeater seal – krill
oss seal – squid
Veddell seal – Antarctic toothfish

ANTARCTICA MEMORY GAME P79–80

. 11 adult penguins
. Two baby penguins
. Asleep
4. Two (Emperor and Adélie)
5. Three
6. Two birds have fish in their beaks.

ODD OCRA OUT P81

FIT FOR A FOX P82

SUDOKU SUPPER P83

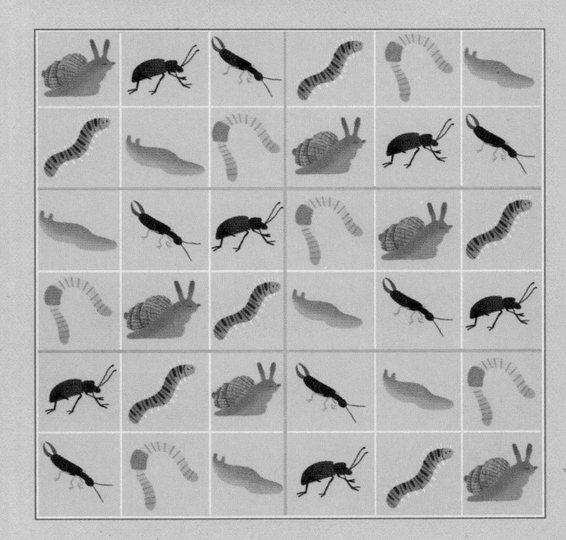

GIRAFFE PATTERN P85

COUNT THE CAPYBARAS P86

There are **29** capybara in the scene.

TANGLED TONGUES P87

A - 4
B - 5
C - 3
D - 1
E - 2

ODD FISH OUT P88

CUBAN CRAB GRID P89

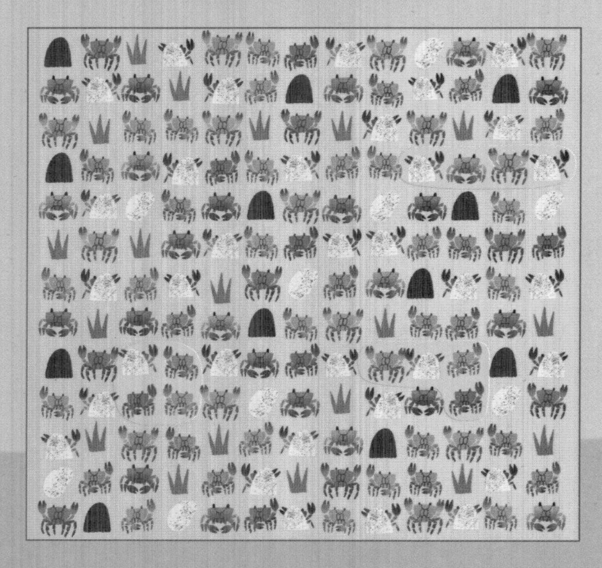

WHOSE EGG IS WHOSE? P90

Cassowary - C
Echidna - D
Emu - A
Duck-billed platypus - B

WHO FLEDGED FIRST? P91

The budgie chicks left the nest in the following order:
D, A, B, C, E

BAMBOO BRAIN-TEASER P92–93

You need to land on the following squares:
B,2; C,4; E,3

SEA OTTER SEARCH P94

SWAMP SUM P95

There are **13** baby alligators missing.

LEAPING LEMURS P96

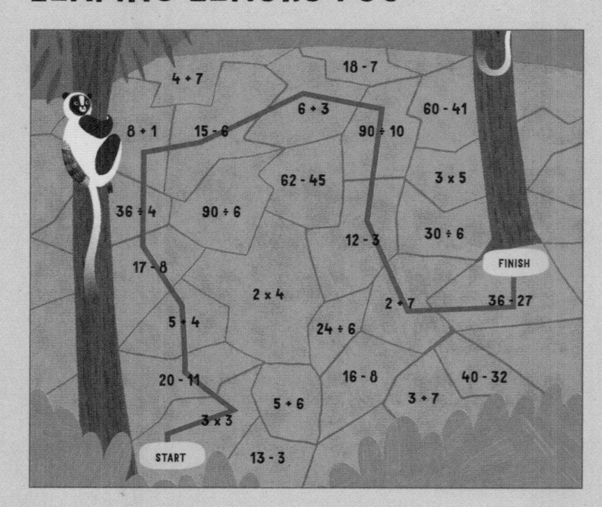

CHAMELEON PAIRS P97

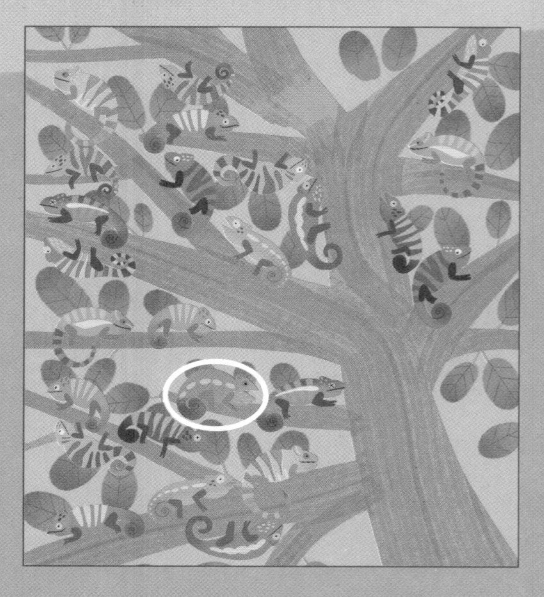

NAKE SUMS P98

x 5 + 4 ÷ 2 = **7 metres**

00 – 4 ÷ 4 + 1 = **25 years**

5 + 6 x 4 + 16 = **100 eggs**

5 x 2 + 40 ÷ 3 = **30 minutes**

RAGON ISLAND P99

. A volcano

. Rocks and a cave

. 5

4. West and there are 4 buffalo

5. 9

ACK WITH THE PACK P100–101

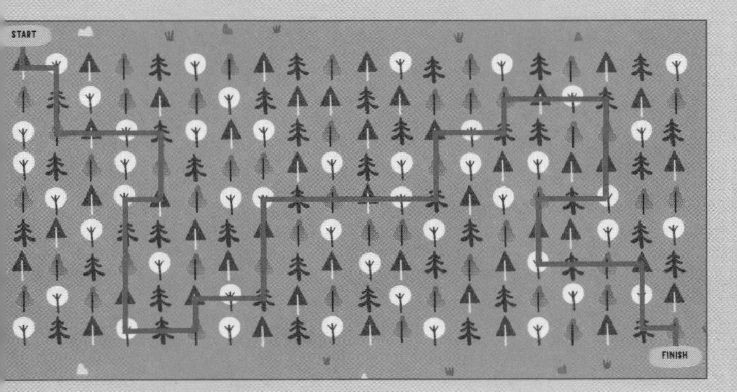

WALLOW MIGRATION P102

he **red barn** is the swallow's final destination.

A BUG'S LIFE P103

PUFFIN MAZE P104

Chick **C** will get the most fish **(7)**. Chick **A** gets **6** fish and Chick **B** gets **4** fish.

HARVEST MICE PICTURE PUZZLE P105

A. G,7
B. H,2
C. B,3
D. H,6
E. C,5
F. G,10
G. C,2
H. D,8

BUTTERFLY LINES P106

DOT-TO-DOT SPOTS P107

The animal is an **ocelot.**

HIPPO STATS P108

75 + 25 x 11 + 200 = **1,300 kg**

100 ÷ 2 - 25 ÷ 5 = **5 minutes**

2 x 6 + 6 - 3 + 20 = **35 kg**

5 x 6 ÷ 2 + 5 = **20 hippos**

AARDVARK CO-ORDINATES P109

1. A tree stump
2. A termite mound
3. A watering hole
4. A lion
5. A forest

RACCOON RAID P110

A - 1

B - 3

C - 4

D - 2

BALD EAGLE REFLECTIONS P111

Reflection **B**

MANGORVE SWAMP SEARCH AND FIND P112–113

There are: **3** Bengal tigers, **2** Ganges river dolphins, **8** mudskippers, **5** brown-winged kingfishers, **7** horseshoe crabs and **6** northern river terrapins.

WHERE'S THE WOODPECKER? P114

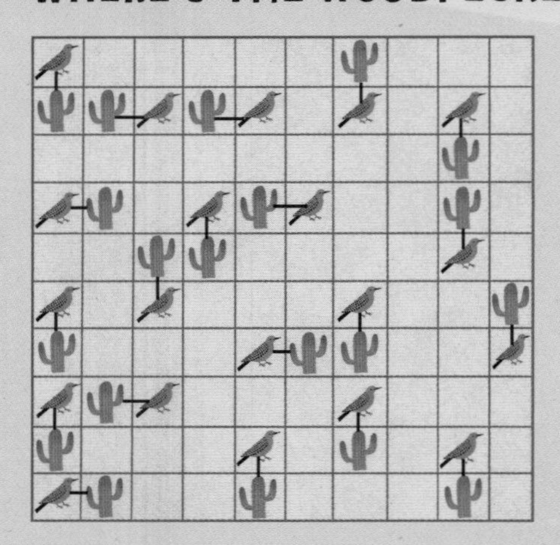

AMERICAN DESERT ANIMALS: TRUE OR FALSE? P115

1. True
2. False – coyotes eat pretty much anything!
3. False – bobcats are solitary.
4. True
5. False – Gila monsters are one of the few venomous lizards.
6. True
7. True
8. False – greater roadrunners can run fast (up to 32 km per hour) but ostriches are the fastest running bird (they can reach speeds of 70 km per hour).
9. True
10. False – desert kit foxes spend most of the day in burrows and hunt at night.

SAVANNA JIGSAW P116–117

Tiles **B**, **G** and **J** are not in the main picture.